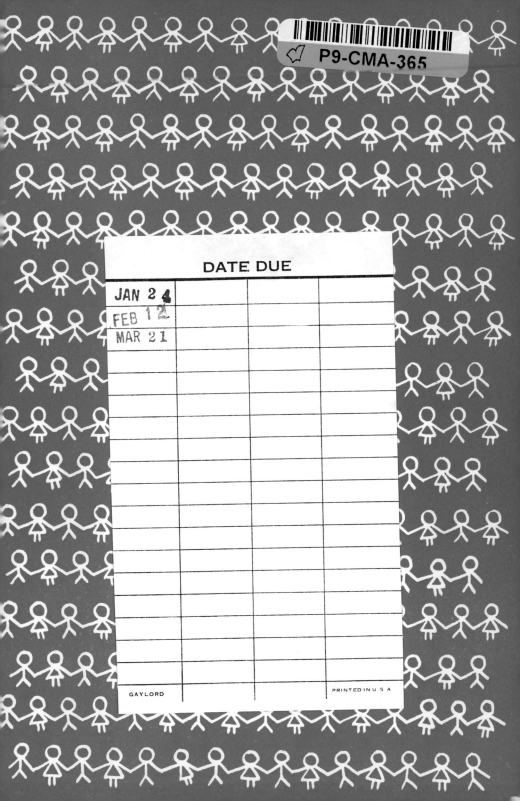

DATE DUE

THE MOON IS SHINING BRIGHT AS DAY

the Moon is shining bright as day

AN ANTHOLOGY OF GOOD-HUMORED VERSE
SELECTED, WITH AN INTRODUCTION, BY

OGDEN NASH

WITH DRAWINGS BY
ROSE SHIRVANIAN

J. B. Lippincott Company
Philadelphia and New York

Printed in the United States of America

Library of Congress Catalog Card Number 53-7143

EIGHTH PRINTING

ACKNOWLEDGEMENTS

Permission to reprint material copyright or controlled by various publishers, agents and individuals has been granted by the following:

HILAIRE BELLOC for "Tarantella."

BOBBS-MERRILL COMPANY, INC. for "Little Orphant Annie" from *Rhymes of Childhood* by James Whitcomb Riley.

CAMBRIDGE UNIVERSITY PRESS for "Keeping On" by A. H. Clough; "The Wind in a Frolic" by William Howitt; "Kitty" by E. Prentiss; "The Maid" by Theodore Roberts; the traditional rhymes "Merry Are the Bells" and "Draw a Pail of Water"; all from *The Cambridge Book of Poetry for Children* edited by Kenneth Grahame.

JONATHAN CAPE, LIMITED and MRS. W. H. DAVIES for "Leisure" and "A Thought" from the *Collected Poems of W. H. Davies;*

JONATHAN CAPE, LIMITED and THE SOCIETY OF AUTHORS for permission to reprint "Yonder See the Morning Blink" from A. E. Housman's *Collected Poems* in the Dominion of Canada.

COWARD-McCANN, INC. for "The Mouse" from *Compass Rose* by Elizabeth Coatsworth. Copyright 1929 by Coward-McCann, Inc. Reprinted by permission.

DOUBLEDAY AND COMPANY, INC. for "The Legends of Evil" from *Departmental Ditties and Ballads and Barrack-Room Ballads* by Rudyard Kipling, reprinted by permission of Mrs. George Bambridge, Doubleday and Company, Inc., the Macmillan Company of Canada, and Methuen and Company; "The Zoo" from *Cursory Rhymes* by Humbert Wolfe, copyright 1927 by Humbert Wolfe, reprinted by permission of Doubleday and Company, Inc. and Miss Anne Wolfe.

iv

ACKNOWLEDGEMENTS

DUELL, SLOAN AND PEARCE, INC. for "Git Along, Little Dogies," words adapted and arranged by John A. and Alan Lomax, reprinted from *Folk Song: U.S.A.*, copyright 1947 by John A. and Alan Lomax, by permission of Duell, Sloan and Pearce, Inc.

KENNETH DURANT for "Millions of Strawberries" by Genevieve Taggard.

E. P. DUTTON AND COMPANY, INC. for "The Three Foxes" and "Missing" from *When We Were Very Young* by A. A. Milne, published and copyright, 1924, by E. P. Dutton and Company, Inc., renewed 1952, A. A. Milne; "Daniel Boone" and "What the Gray Cat Sings" from *I Sing the Pioneer* by Arthur Guiterman, published and copyright, 1926, by E. P. Dutton and Company, Inc.; "Of Tact" from *A Poet's Proverbs* by Arthur Guiterman, copyright, 1924, by E. P. Dutton and Company, Inc., renewed 1952, Mrs. Arthur Guiterman.

FABER AND FABER, LIMITED for permission to reprint "Prelude" (I) from *Collected Poems of T. S. Eliot* in the Dominion of Canada.

HARCOURT, BRACE AND COMPANY, INC. for "Chanson Innocent" by E. E. Cummings from *Collected Poems* published by Harcourt, Brace and Company, Inc., copyright, 1923, by E. E. Cummings; "Prelude" (I) from *Collected Poems of T. S. Eliot*, copyright, 1936, by Harcourt, Brace and Company, Inc.; "Primer Lesson" from *Early Moon* by Carl Sandburg, copyright, 1930, by Harcourt, Brace and Company, Inc.; "Wind Song" from *Smoke and Steel* by Carl Sandburg, copyright, 1920, by Harcourt, Brace and Company, Inc.

HARPER AND BROTHERS for "Portrait by a Neighbor" from *A Few Figs from Thistles* published by Harper and Brothers, copyright, 1920, 1948, by Edna St. Vincent Millay; "The Unexplorer" from *A Few Figs from Thistles* published by Harper and Brothers, copyright, 1918, 1946, by Edna St. Vincent Millay; "Travel" from *Second April* published by Harper and Brothers, copyright, 1921, 1949, by Edna St. Vincent Millay; "Counting-out Rhyme" from *A Buck in the Snow* published by Harper and Brothers, copyright, 1928, by Edna St. Vincent Millay.

HENRY HOLT AND COMPANY, INC. for "Psalm of Those Who Go Forth Before Daylight" from *Cornhuskers* by Carl Sandburg, copyright, 1918, by Henry Holt and Company, Inc., copyright, 1946, by Carl Sandburg; "Yonder See the Morning Blink" from *Last Poems* by A. E. Housman, copyright, 1922, by Henry Holt and Company, Inc., copyright, 1950, by Barclays Bank, Limited; "Miss T," "Tired Tim," "Summer Evening," "The Mocking Fairy," "Bunches of Grapes," and "Some One" from *Collected Poems* by Walter de la Mare, copyright, 1920, by Henry Holt and Company, Inc., copyright, 1948, by Walter de la Mare; "At a Country Fair" from *Fair Warning* by John Holmes, copyright, 1939, by Henry Holt and Company, Inc.; "Stopping by Woods on a Snowy Evening," "The Pasture" and "Dust of Snow" from *Complete Poems of Robert Frost*, copyright, 1930, 1949, by Henry Holt and Company, Inc.; "Charlie Chaplin Went to France"

ACKNOWLEDGEMENTS

from *A Rocket in My Pocket* by Carl Withers. All used by permission of the publishers.

ALFRED A. KNOPF, INC. for "The Frog" and "The Big Baboon" reprinted from *Cautionary Verses* by Hilaire Belloc, by permission of Alfred A. Knopf, Inc. Copyright 1931 by Hilaire Belloc.

T. WERNER LAURIE, LIMITED for "Lord Clive" and "Sir Christopher Wren" from *Clerihews Complete* by E. C. Bentley, copyright 1951.

J. B. LIPPINCOTT COMPANY for "At the Dog Show (To an Irish Wolfhound)" from *Songs for a Little House* by Christopher Morley, copyright, 1917, 1945, by Christopher Morley, published by J. B. Lippincott Company.

LITTLE, BROWN AND COMPANY for "Lightly Stepped a Yellow Star," copyright 1914 by Martha Dickinson Bianchi; "Hope Is the Thing With Feathers," "A Bird Came Down the Walk," "I Like to See It Lap the Miles" and "I'll Tell You How the Sun Rose" from *Poems by Emily Dickinson*, edited by Martha Dickinson Bianchi and Alfred Leete Hampson, by permission of Little, Brown and Company; "The Duck," "The Germ," "The Wapiti," "The Kitten," "The Panther" and "Adventures of Isabel" from *Many Long Years Ago* by Ogden Nash; "An Introduction to Dogs" and "The Purist" from *I'm A Stranger Here Myself* by Ogden Nash, by permission of Little, Brown and Company. Copyright by Ogden Nash: The Duck 1936; The Germ 1935; An Introduction to Dogs 1939; The Purist 1939; The Wapiti 1933; The Kitten 1940; The Panther 1940; Adventures of Isabel 1936.

DAVID McKAY COMPANY, INC. for "Miss James" from *A Gallery of Children* by A. A. Milne. Copyright, 1925, by David McKay Company, Inc., and reprinted with their permission.

THE MACMILLAN COMPANY for "On a Night of Snow" from Elizabeth Coatsworth's *Night and the Cat*, copyright 1950 by The Macmillan Company; "Luck" from Wilfrid Gibson's *I Heard a Sailor*, copyright 1925 by The Macmillan Company; "Time, You Old Gypsy Man" and "The Great Auk's Ghost" from Ralph Hodgson's *Poems*, copyright 1945 by The Macmillan Company; "The Falling Star" from Sara Teasdale's *Collected Poems*, copyright 1930 by Sara Teasdale; "The Shell" and "White Fields" from James Stephens' *Collected Poems*, copyright 1909 by The Macmillan Company; "The Tutor" and "The Grandiloquent Goat" from Carolyn Wells' *The Jingle Book*, copyright 1899, 1927 by The Macmillan Company; all used with the permission of The Macmillan Company.

MACMILLAN AND COMPANY LIMITED OF LONDON for permission to reprint "The Shell" and "White Fields" from James Stephens' *Collected Poems* in the Dominion of Canada; MACMILLAN AND COMPANY LIMITED OF LONDON and MISS NANCY McINTOSH for permission to reprint "The Yarn of the Nancy Bell" from W. S. Gilbert's *Bab Ballads* in the Dominion of Canada.

ACKNOWLEDGEMENTS

METHUEN AND COMPANY for "The Dancing Cabman" from By the Way by J. B. Morton (Beachcomber of The London Daily Express) by permission of Methuen and Company; for "Patience" by Captain Harry Graham from The World We Laugh In, by permission of the executrix and Methuen and Company.

THE NEW YORK TIMES for "Queen Anne's Lace" by Mary Leslie Newton, Dean 1916–37, All Saints' Episcopal Junior College, Vicksburg, Mississippi. Copyright July 9, 1923.

ORWELL PRESS for "A Piper" from Collected Poems by Seumas O'Sullivan, published by Orwell Press, 1940.

PUNCH for "A Roundabout Turn" by Robert H. Charles, reproduced by permission of the Proprietors of Punch.

G. P. PUTNAM'S SONS for "Blum" from Here, There and Everywhere by Dorothy Aldis, copyright 1927 by Dorothy Aldis. Reprinted by permission of G. P. Putnam's Sons.

REMINGTON BOOK STORES, Baltimore, Maryland for "The Good Joan" from Spicewood by Lizette Woodworth Reese.

RINEHART AND COMPANY, INC. for "Gentle Name" from City Child, copyright, 1931, by Selma Robinson, and reprinted by permission of Rinehart and Company, Inc., publishers.

HAMILTON RICHARDS, trustee u/w Laura E. Richards for "Antonio" by Laura E. Richards, from Child Life Magazine, copyright, 1936.

THE HON. V. SACKVILLE-WEST for "Full Moon" from Collected Poems by V. Sackville-West, published by Hogarth Press, 1933.

CHARLES SCRIBNER'S SONS for "Ducks' Ditty" reprinted from The Wind in the Willows by Kenneth Grahame, copyright 1908, 1935 by Charles Scribner's Sons, used by permission of the publishers; "The Duel" from Poems of Childhood by Eugene Field.

SIMPKIN MARSHALL, LIMITED for "Overheard on a Saltmarsh" by Harold Monro.

MRS. EDWARD THOMAS for "If I Should Ever by Chance" from The Collected Poems of Edward Thomas, published by Faber and Faber, Limited.

THE VIKING PRESS, INC. for "The Good Humor Man" and "Ballroom Dancing Class" from A Short Walk to the Station by Phyllis McGinley, copyright 1947, 1951 by Phyllis McGinley. These poems originally appeared in The New Yorker. Reprinted by permission of The Viking Press, Inc., New York.

FREDERICK WARNE AND COMPANY, LIMITED, London and New York for "Ring-a-Ring," "The Boat Sails Away," "Five Little Sisters Walking in a Row," and "Will You Be My Little Wife" by Kate Greenaway.

FOREWORD

This year found me on my fourth and probably last lecture tour. One recent night stands out in my memory. I had completed my sixty minutes of artfully assorted chitchat and poetry, and was gratified to find that as I returned to my chair the majority of the audience was still in theirs, or its. Something accomplished, I thought, something done; now for a night's repose before catching the 5:30 A.M. local to Chicago. I dimpled with diffident anticipation as the chairman arose to terminate the session. "I am sure," he said, "that we all enjoyed hearing our celebrated guest speak and speak and speak, and read verse after verse after verse."

As I write these lines I feel premonitory symptoms of the hot and cold goose flesh that enswaddled me on that occasion. In a world already listless from the impact of anthology after anthology after anthology I assume responsibility for another; it seems possible that I have outworn my welcome before entering the room. If my temerity is too brazen to be excused, perhaps it can at least be explained.

It had never occurred to me to set up as a practising anthologist, but when the suggestion was made that I assemble a collection of not too serious poems for boys and girls I easily fell in with it. Perhaps "assemble" is the wrong word; "remember" would be better. As a man moves into his fifties he becomes increasingly aware of the reading that illuminated his childhood, and the temptation to pass a good thing along is irresistible. That is why there are few rare specimens in this collection, which has been gathered from the daisies rather than the orchids. The older poems here are ones that gave me pleasure as a boy, and the newer ones were introduced to me by my children when we started reading together.

For better or worse, I have followed as an anthologist the course, and the only course, that enabled me to set pencil to paper as a writer; that is, to proceed as if nothing had ever been written before. The fact that everything you have to say has been said earlier and better is a paralyzing one, and the only thing to do is ignore it, and assume that you are living in the first day of the world.

Few of the poems in this collection are outright comic, and few are serious in the pedantic sense, yet to me most of them have that indefinable but unmistakable feel that lets you know you are handling the genuine article. If they do not, like "Ode on a Grecian Urn," ride the heavens with the bright majesty of the winter moon, they are comparable to the strange and unearthly shadows she casts, and fun to play among.

This would be a less helter-skelter book but for the death of Miss Helen Dean Fish, whose wide experience, firm editorial hand, and patient kindness are irreplaceable. Left to myself, I retire quoting an English advertisement which, except for the name of the product, expresses my feelings about this unpretentious volume.

> I see you drink Jones's. Nice bottle.
> *Nice ginger beer.*
> What's the difference between Jones's
> and any other ginger beer?
> *I haven't the slightest idea.*
> Then why drink it?
> *Because I like it.*
> That's not a very very profound reason.
> *It's the best I can do. Try it*
> *and see if you can think of a*
> *better one.*
>
> Ogden Nash

Contents

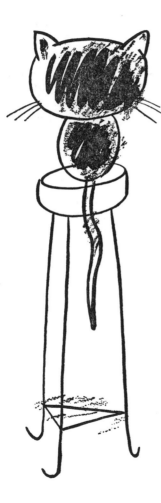

Girls and boys, come out to play,
The moon is shining bright as day.
Leave your supper, and leave your sleep,
And come with your playfellows into the street,
Come with a whoop, come with a call,
Come with a good will or not at all.
Up the ladder and down the wall,
A halfpenny roll will serve us all;
You find milk, and I'll find flour,
And we'll have a pudding in half-an-hour.
Mother Goose

1

HAS ANYBODY SEEN MY MOUSE?

Three Things to Remember

WILLIAM BLAKE

A Robin Redbreast in a cage,
Puts all Heaven in a rage.

A skylark wounded on the wing
Doth make a cherub cease to sing.

He who shall hurt the little wren
Shall never be beloved by men.

The Story of Augustus Who Would Not Have Any Soup

HEINRICH HOFFMANN

Augustus was a chubby lad;
Fat ruddy cheeks Augustus had;
And everybody saw with joy,
The plump and hearty healthy boy.
He ate and drank as he was told,
And never let his soup get cold.
But one day, one cold winter's day,
He screamed out—"Take the soup away!
O take the nasty soup away!
I won't have any soup today!"

How lank and lean Augustus grows!
Next day he scarcely fills his clothes,
Yet, though he feels so weak and ill,
The naughty fellow cries out still—
"Not any soup for me, I say:
O take the nasty soup away!
I won't have any soup today!"

The third day comes; ah! what a sin!
To make himself so pale and thin.
Yet, when the soup is put on table,
He screams, as loud as he is able,
"Not any soup for me, I say:
O take the nasty soup away!
I won't have any soup today!"

Look at him, now the fourth day's come!
He scarcely weighs a sugar-plum;
He's like a little bit of thread,
And on the fifth day he was—dead!

The Frog

HILAIRE BELLOC

Be kind and tender to the Frog,
    And do not call him names,
As, 'Slimy-skin,' or 'Polly-wog,'
    Or likewise, 'Uncle James,'
Or 'Gape-a-grin,' or 'Toad-gone-wrong,'
    Or 'Billy-Bandy-Knees':
The frog is justly sensitive
    To epithets like these.

No animal will more repay
    A treatment kind and fair,
At least so lonely people say
    Who keep a frog (and by the way,
They are extremely rare.)

The Grandiloquent Goat

CAROLYN WELLS

A very grandiloquent goat
    Sat down to a gay table d'hote;
        He ate all the corks,
        The knives and the forks,
Remarking, "On these things I dote."

Then before his repast he began,
    While pausing the menu to scan,
        He said, "Corn, if you please,
        And tomatoes and pease,
I'd like to have served in the can."

A Good Play

ROBERT LOUIS STEVENSON

We built a ship upon the stairs
All made of the back-bedroom chairs,
And filled it full of sofa pillows
To go a-sailing on the billows.

We took a saw and several nails,
And water in the nursery pails;
And Tom said, "Let us also take
An apple and a slice of cake;"—
Which was enough for Tom and me
To go a-sailing on, till tea.

We sailed along for days and days
And had the very best of plays
But Tom fell out and hurt his knee,
So there was no one left but me.

Patience

HARRY GRAHAM

When ski-ing in the Engadine
My hat blew off down a ravine.
My son, who went to fetch it back,
Slipped through an icy glacier's crack,
And then got permanently stuck.
It really was infernal luck;
My hat was practically new—
I loved my little Henry too—
And I may have to wait for years
Till either of them reappears.

5

The Three Welshmen

OLD RHYME

There were three jovial Welshmen,
As I have heard them say,
And they would go a-hunting
Upon St. David's day.

All the day they hunted,
And nothing could they find
But a ship a-sailing,
A-sailing with the wind.

One said it was a ship;
The other he said nay;
The third said it was a house,
With the chimney blown away.

And all night they hunted,
And nothing could they find
But the moon a-gliding,
A-gliding with the wind.

One said it was the moon;
The other he said nay;
The third said it was a cheese,
And half o't cut away.

And all the day they hunted,
And nothing could they find
But a hedgehog in a bramble-bush,
And that they left behind.

The first said it was a hedgehog,
The second he said nay;

The third it was a pin-cushion,
And the pins stuck the wrong way.

And all the night they hunted,
And nothing could they find
But a hare in a turnip field,
And that they left behind.

The first said it was a hare;
The second he said nay;
The third said it was a calf,
And the cow had run away.

And all the day they hunted,
And nothing could they find
But an owl in a holly-tree,
And that they left behind.

One said it was an owl;
The other he said nay;
The third said 'twas an old man,
And his beard growing grey.

Days of Birth

OLD RHYME

Monday's child is fair of face,
Tuesday's child is full of grace,
Wednesday's child is full of woe,
Thursday's child has far to go,
Friday's child is loving and giving,
Saturday's child works for its living,
And a child that's born on the Sabbath day
Is fair and wise and good and gay.

Two Magpies Sat on a Garden Rail

D'A. W. THOMPSON

Two Magpies sat on a garden rail,
    As it might be Wednesday week;
And one little Magpie wagged his tail
    In the other little Magpie's beak.

And, doubling like a fist his little claw-hand,
    Said this other, "Upon my word,
This is more than flesh and blood can stand
    Of Magpie or any other bird."

So they picked and they scratched each other's little eyes,
    Till all that was left on the rail
Was the beak of one of the little Magpies,
    And the other little Magpie's tail.

The Windmill

HENRY WADSWORTH LONGFELLOW

Behold! a giant am I!
Aloft here in my tower,
With my granite jaws I devour
The maize, and the wheat and the rye,
    And grind them into flour.

I look down over the farms;
    In the fields of grain I see
    The harvest that is to be,
And I fling to the air my arms,
    For I know it is all for me.

I hear the sound of flails
    Far off, from the threshing-floors
    In barns, with their open doors,
And the wind, the wind in my sails,
    Louder and louder roars.

I stand here in my place,
    With my foot on the rock below,
    And whichever way it may blow
I meet it face to face,
    As a brave man meets his foe.

And while we wrestle and strive,
    My master, the miller, stands
    And feeds me with his hands;
For he knows who makes him thrive,
    Who makes him lord of lands.

On Sundays I take my rest;
    Church-going bells begin
    Their low, melodious din;
I cross my arms on my breast,
    And all is peace within.

Primer Lesson

CARL SANDBURG

Look out how you use proud words.
When you let proud words go, it is not easy to call them
        back.
They wear long boots, hard boots; they walk off proud;
They can't hear you calling—
Look out how you use proud words.

Missing

A. A. MILNE

Has anybody seen my mouse?

I opened his box for half a minute,
Just to make sure he was really in it,
And while I was looking, he jumped outside!
I tried to catch him, I tried, I tried. . . .
I think he's somewhere about the house.
Has *anyone* seen my mouse?

Uncle John, have you seen my mouse?

Just a small sort of mouse, a dear little brown one,
He came from the country, he wasn't a town one,
So he'll feel all lonely in a London street;
Why, what could he possibly find to eat?

He must be somewhere. I'll ask Aunt Rose:
Have *you* seen a mouse with a woffelly nose?
Oh, somewhere about—
He's just got out . . .

Hasn't *anybody* seen my mouse?

A Tragic Story

WILLIAM MAKEPEACE THACKERAY

There lived a sage in days of yore,
And he a handsome pigtail wore;
But wondered much, and sorrowed more,
    Because it hung behind him.

He mused upon this curious case,
And swore he'd change the pigtail's place,
And have it hanging at his face,
    Not dangling there behind him.

Says he, "The mystery I've found,—
I'll turn me round,"—he turned him round,
    But still it hung behind him.

Then round and round, and out and in,
All day the puzzled sage did spin;
In vain—it mattered not a pin—
    The pigtail hung behind him.

And right and left, and round about,
And up and down and in and out

He turned; but still the pigtail stout
    Hung steadily behind him.

And though his efforts never slack,
And though he twist, and twirl, and tack,
Alas! still faithful to his back,
    The pigtail hangs behind him.

Hector Protector

OLD RHYME

Hector Protector was dressed all in green;
Hector Protector was sent to the Queen.
The Queen did not like him, no more did the King;
So Hector Protector was sent back again.

The Big Baboon

HILAIRE BELLOC

The Big Baboon is found upon
    The plains of Cariboo;
He goes about
      with nothing on
(A shocking thing to do).
But if he
      dressed respectably
And let his whiskers grow,
How like this Big Baboon would be
    To Mister So-and-so!

There Was an Old Woman

OLD RHYME

There was an old woman, as I've heard tell,
She went to market her eggs for to sell;
She went to market all on a market day,·
And she fell asleep on the king's highway.

There came a peddler whose name was Stout,
He cut her petticoats all round about;
He cut her petticoats up to the knees,
Which made the old woman shiver and freeze.

When this little old woman first did wake,
She began to shiver and she began to shake;
She began to wonder and she began to cry,
"O! deary, deary me, this is none of I!"

"But if it be I as I hope it be,
I've a little dog at home, and he'll know me;
If it be I, he'll wag his tail
And if it be not I, he'll loudly bark and wail!"

Home went the little woman all in the dark,
Up got the little dog, and he began to bark;
He began to bark; so she began to cry,
"O! deary, deary me, this is none of I!"

The Wapiti

OGDEN NASH

There goes the Wapiti,
Hippety-hoppity!

What the Gray Cat Sings

ARTHUR GUITERMAN

The Cat was once a weaver,
    A weaver, a weaver,
An old and withered weaver
    Who labored late and long;
And while she made the shuttle hum
And wove the weft and clipped the thrum,
Beside the loom with droning drum
    She sang the weaving song:
        "Pr-rrum, pr-rrum,
Thr-ree thr-reads in the thr-rum,
        Pr-rrum!"

The Cat's no more a weaver,
    A weaver, a weaver,
An old and wrinkled weaver,
    For though she did no wrong,
A witch hath changed the shape of her
That dwindled down and clothed in fur
Beside the hearth with droning purr
    She thrums her weaving song:
        "Pr-rrum, pr-rrum,
Thr-ree thr-reads in the thr-rum,
        Pr-rrum!"

Home

J. H. GORING

The Germans live in Germany;
The Romans live in Rome;
The Turkeys live in Turkey
But the English live at home.

Miss T.

WALTER DE LA MARE

It's a very odd thing—
　　As odd as can be—
That whatever Miss T. eats
　　Turns into Miss T.;
Porridge and apples,
　　Minces, muffins, and mutton,
Jam, junket, jumbles—
　　Not a rap, not a button
It matters; the moment
　　They're out of her plate,
Though shared by Miss Butcher
　　And sour Mr. Bate;
Tiny and cheerful,
　　And as neat as can be,
Whatever Miss T. eats
　　Turns into Miss T.

An Introduction to Dogs

OGDEN NASH

The dog is man's best friend.
He has a tail on one end.
Up in front he has teeth.
And four legs underneath.

Dogs like to bark.
They like it best after dark.
They not only frighten prowlers away
But also hold the sandman at bay.

A dog that is indoors
To be let out implores.
You let him out and what then?
He wants back in again.

Dogs display reluctance and wrath
If you try to give them a bath.
They bury bones in hideaways
And half the time they trot sideaways.

They cheer up people who are frowning,
And rescue people who are drowning,
They also track mud on beds,
And chew people's clothes to shreds.

Dogs in the country have fun.
They run and run and run.
But in the city this species
Is dragged around on leashes.

Dogs are upright as a steeple
And much more loyal than people.
Well people may be reprehensibler
But that's probably because they are sensibler.

How To Write a Letter

ELIZABETH TURNER

Maria intended a letter to write,
But could not begin (as she thought) to indite;
So went to her mother with pencil and slate,
Containing "Dear Sister," and also a date.

16

"With nothing to say, my dear girl, do not think
Of wasting your time over paper and ink;
But certainly this is an excellent way,
To try with your slate to find something to say.

"I will give you a rule," said her Mother: "My dear,
Just think for a moment your sister is here,
And what would you tell her? Consider, and then,
Though silent your tongue, you can speak with your pen."

How Doth the Little Crocodile

LEWIS CARROLL

How doth the little crocodile
    Improve his shining tail,
And pour the waters of the Nile
    On every golden scale!

How cheerfully he seems to grin,
    How neatly spreads his claws,
And welcomes little fishes in
    With gently smiling jaws!

A Child's Grace

ROBERT BURNS

Some hae meat and canna eat,
    And some wad eat that want it;
But we hae meat and we can eat,
    And sae the Lord be thankit.

The Good Humor Man

PHYLLIS MCGINLEY

Listen! It is the summer's self that ambles
    Through the green lanes with such a coaxing tongue.
Not birds or daisy fields were ever symbols
    More proper to the time than this bell rung
With casual insistence—no, not swallow
    Circling the roof or bee in hollyhock.
His is the season's voice, the children follow,
    Panting, from every doorway down the block.

So, long ago, in some such shrill procession
    Perhaps the Hamelin children gave pursuit
To one who wore a red-and-yellow fashion
    Instead of white, but made upon his flute
The selfsame promise plain to every comer:
Unending sweets, imperishable summer.

The Old Man Who Lived in a Wood

OLD RHYME

There was an old man who lived in a wood,
    As you may plainly see;
He said he could do as much work in a day,
    As his wife could do in three.
"With all my heart," the old woman said,
    "If that you will allow,
Tomorrow you'll stay at home in my stead,
    And I'll go drive the plough;

"But you must milk the Tidy cow,
    For fear that she go dry;
And you must feed the little pigs
    That are within the sty;
And you must mind the speckled hen,
    For fear she lay away;
And you must reel the spool of yarn
    That I spun yesterday."

The old woman took a staff in her hand,
    And went to drive the plough;
The old man took a pail in his hand,
    And went to milk the cow;
But Tidy hinched, and Tidy flinched,
    And Tidy broke his nose,
And Tidy gave him such a blow,
    That the blood ran down to his toes.

"High! Tidy! ho! Tidy! high!
    Tidy, do stand still!
If ever I milk you, Tidy, again,
    'T will be sore against my will."

He went to feed the little pigs,
    That were within the sty;
He hit his head against the beam
    And he made the blood to fly.

He went to mind the speckled hen,
    For fear she'd lay astray,
And he forgot the spool of yarn
    His wife spun yesterday.

So he swore by the sun, the moon, and the stars,
    And the green leaves on the tree,
If his wife didn't do a day's work in her life,
    She should ne'er be ruled by he.

The Lost Doll

CHARLES KINGSLEY

I once had a sweet little doll, dears,
    The prettiest doll in the world;
Her cheeks were so red and white, dears,
    And her hair was so charmingly curled.
But I lost my poor little doll, dears,
    As I played on the heath one day;
And I cried for her more than a week, dears,
    But I never could find where she lay.

I found my poor little doll, dears,
    As I played on the heath one day;
Folks say she is terribly changed, dears,
    For her paint is all washed away,
And her arms trodden off by the cows, dears,
And her hair not the least bit curled;
Yet for old sake's sake, she is still, dears,
    The prettiest doll in the world.

The Boat Sails Away

KATE GREENAWAY

The boat sails away, like a bird on the wing,
And the little boys dance on the sands in a ring.

The wind may fall, or the wind may rise—
You are foolish to go; you will stay if you're wise.

The little boys dance, and the little girls run;
If it's bad to have money, it's worse to have none.

This Is the Key

AUTHOR UNKNOWN

This is the Key of the Kingdom:
In that Kingdom is a city;
In that city is a town;
In that town there is a street;
In that street there winds a lane;
In that lane there is a yard;
In that yard there is a house;
In that house there waits a room;
In that room an empty bed;
And on that bed a basket—
A Basket of Sweet Flowers:
    Of Flowers, of Flowers;
    A Basket of Sweet Flowers.

Flowers in a basket;
Basket on the bed;
Bed in the chamber;
Chamber in the house;
House in the weedy yard;
Yard in the winding lane;
Lane in the broad street;
Street in the high town;
Town in the city;
City in the Kingdom—
This is the Key of the Kingdom;
    Of the Kingdom this is the Key.

Bunches of Grapes

WALTER DE LA MARE

"Bunches of grapes," says Timothy;
    "Pomegranates pink," says Elaine;
"A junket of cream and a cranberry tart
    For me," says Jane.

"Love-in-a-mist," says Timothy;
    "Primroses pale," says Elaine;
"A nosegay of pinks and migonette
    For me," says Jane.

"Chariots of gold," says Timothy;
    "Silvery wings," says Elaine;
"A bumpity ride in a waggon of hay
    For me," says Jane.

The Wind and the Moon

GEORGE MACDONALD

Said the Wind to the Moon, "I will blow you out;
            You stare
            In the air
            Like a ghost in a chair,
Always looking what I am about—
I hate to be watched; I'll blow you out."

The Wind blew hard, and out went the Moon.
            So deep
            On a heap
            Of clouds to sleep,
Down lay the Wind, and slumbered soon,
Muttering low, "I've done for that Moon."

He turned in his bed; she was there again!
  On high
  In the sky,
  With her one ghost eye,
The moon shone white and alive and plain.
Said the Wind, "I'll blow you out again."

The Wind blew hard, and the Moon grew dim.
  "With my sledge
  And my wedge,
  I have knocked off her edge!
If only I blow right fierce and grim,
The creature will soon be dimmer than dim."

He blew and he blew, and she thinned to a thread.
  "One puff
  More's enough
  To blow her to snuff!
First blew her away right out of the sky,
Then blew her in. What strength have I!"

But the moon she knew nothing about the affair;
  For high
  In the sky,
  With her one eye,
Motionless, miles above the air,
She had never heard the great Wind blare.

The Kitten

OGDEN NASH

The trouble with a kitten is
THAT
Eventually it becomes a
CAT.

There Was a Wee Bit Mousikie

SCOTTISH NURSERY RHYME

There was a wee bit mousikie,
    That lived in Gilberaty, O,
It couldna get a bit o' cheese,
    For cheetie-pussie-cattie, O.

It said unto the cheesikie,
    "Oh, fain would I be at ye, O,
"If it were na for the cruel paws
    "Oh, cheetie-pussie-cattie, O!"

The Moo-Cow-Moo

EDMUND VANCE COOKE

My pa held me up to the moo-cow-moo
    So clost I could almost touch,
En I fed him a couple of times, or two,
    En I wasn't a fraid-cat—much.

But ef my papa goes into the house,
    En mama she goes in, too,
I just keep still, like a little mouse,
    Fer the moo-cow-moo might moo!

The moo-cow-moo's got a tail like a rope
    En it's raveled down where it grows,
En it's just like feeling a piece of soap
    All over the moo-cow's nose.

En the moo-cow-moo has lots of fun
    Just swinging his tail about;
En he opens his mouth and then I run—
    'Cause that's where the moo comes out!

24

En the moo-cow-moo's got deers on his head
　　En his eyes stick out of their place;
En the nose of the moo-cow is spread
　　All over the end of his face.

En his feet is nothing but finger nails
　　En his mama don't keep 'em cut,
En he gives folks milk in water-pails
　　Ef he don't keep his handles shut.

'Cause if you er me pulls the handles, why
　　The moo-cow-moo says it hurts,
But the hired man he sits down clost by
　　En squirts en squirts en squirts!

The Pobble Who Has No Toes

EDWARD LEAR

The Pobble who has no toes
　　Had once as many as we;
When they said, 'Some day you may lose them all;'—
　　He replied,—'Fish fiddle de-dee!'
And his Aunt Jobiska made him drink,
Lavender water tinged with pink,
For she said, 'The World in general knows
There's nothing so good for a Pobble's toes!'

The Pobble who has no toes,
　　Swam across the Bristol Channel;
But before he set out he wrapped his nose,
　　In a piece of scarlet flannel.
For his Aunt Jobiska said, 'No harm
'Can come to his toes if his nose is warm;
'And it's perfectly known that a Pobble's toes
'Are safe,—provided he minds his nose.'

The Pobble swam fast and well
And when boats or ships came near him
He tinkledly-binkledy-winkled a bell
So that all the world could hear him.
And all the Sailors and Admirals cried,
When they saw him nearing the further side,
'He has gone to fish, for his Aunt Jobiska's
'Runcible Cat with crimson whiskers!'

But before he touched the shore,
The shore of the Bristol Channel,
A sea-green Porpoise carried away
His wrapper of scarlet flannel.
And when he came to observe his feet
Formerly garnished with toes so neat
His face at once became forlorn
On perceiving that all his toes were gone!

And nobody ever knew
From that dark day to the present,
Whoso had taken the Pobble's toes,
In a manner so far from pleasant.
Whether the shrimps or crawfish gray,
Or crafty Mermaids stole them away—
Nobody knew; and nobody knows
How the Pobble was robbed of his twice five toes!

The Pobble who has no toes
Was placed in a friendly Bark,
And they rowed him back, and carried him up,
To his Aunt Jobiska's Park.
And she made him a feast at his earnest wish
Of eggs and buttercups fried with fish;
And she said, "It's a fact the whole world knows,
That Pobbles are happier without their toes."

Pigwiggin Arms Himself

MICHAEL DRAYTON

He quickly arms him for the field,
A little cockle-shell his shield,
Which he could very bravely wield,
    Yet could it not be piercèd.
His spear a bent both stiff and strong,
And well-near of two inches long:
The pile was of a horsefly's tongue,
    Whose sharpness nought reversèd.

And puts him on a coat of mail,
Which was of a fish's scale,
That when his foe should him assail,
    No point should be prevailing:
His rapier was a hornet's sting;
It was a very dangerous thing,
For if he chanced to hurt the king,
    It would be long in healing.

His helmet was a beetle's head,
Most horrible and full of dread,
That able was to strike one dead,
    Yet did it well become him.
And for a plume a horse's hair
Which, being tossèd with the air,
Had force to strike his foe with fear,
    And turn his weapon from him.

Himself he on an earwig set,
Yet scarce he on his back could get,
So oft and high he did curvet,
    Ere he himself could settle:

He made him turn, and stop, and bound,
To gallop and to trot the round,
He scarce could stand on any ground,
    He was so full of mettle.

The Snail

CHARLES LAMB

The frugal snail, with forecast of repose,
Carries his house with him wher'er he goes;
Peeps out,—and if there comes a shower of rain,
Retreats to his small domicile again.
Touch but a tip of him, a horn,—'tis well,—
He curls up in his sanctuary shell.
He's his own landlord, his own tenant; stay
Long as he will, he dreads no quarter day.
Himself he boards and lodges; both invites
And feasts himself; sleeps with himself o'nights.
He spares the upholsterer trouble to procure
Chattels; himself is his own furniture,
And his sole riches. Wheresoe'er he roam,—
Knock when you will,—he's sure to be at home.

Aunt Maud

AUTHOR UNKNOWN

I had written to Aunt Maud
Who was on a trip abroad,
When I heard she'd died of cramp
Just too late to save the stamp.

Incidents in the Life of My Uncle Arly

EDWARD LEAR

O my agèd Uncle Arly!
Sitting on a heap of Barley
    Thro' the silent hours of night,
Close beside a leafy thicket.
On his nose there was a Cricket,
In his hat a Railway-Ticket;
    (But his shoes were far too tight).

Long ago, in youth, he squander'd
All his goods away, and wander'd
    To the Tiniskoop-hills afar.
There on golden sunsets blazing,
Every evening found him gazing,
Singing: "Orb! you're quite amazing!
    How I wonder what you are!"

Like the ancient Medes and Persians,
Always by his own exertions
    He subsisted on those hills;
Whiles, by teaching children spelling,
Or at times by merely yelling,
Or at intervals by selling
    "Propter's Nicodemus Pills."

Later, in his morning rambles
He perceived the moving brambles
    Something square and white disclose.
'Twas a First-class Railway-Ticket;
But, on stooping down to pick it
Off the ground, a pea-green Cricket
    Settled on my uncle's Nose.

Never—never more—oh! never,
Did that Cricket leave him ever,
    Dawn or evening, day or night;
Clinging as a constant treasure,
Chirping with a cheerious measure,
Wholly to my uncle's pleasure,
    (Though his shoes were far too tight).

So for three-and-forty winters,
Till his shoes were worn to splinters,
    All those hills he wander'd o'er,
Sometimes silent, sometimes yelling,
Till he came to Borley-Melling,
Near his old ancestral dwelling;
    (But his shoes were far too tight).

On a little heap of Barley
Died my agèd Uncle Arly,
    And they buried him one night,
Close beside the leafy thicket;
There his hat and Railway-Ticket;
There his ever-faithful Cricket;
    (But his shoes were far too tight).

A Swing Song

WILLIAM ALLINGHAM

    Swing, swing,
    Sing, sing,
Here! my throne and I am a king!
    Swing, sing,
    Swing, sing,
Farewell, earth, for I'm on the wing!

30

Low, high,
Here I fly,
Like a bird through sunny sky;
Free, free,
Over the lea,
Over the mountain, over the sea!

Up, down,
Up and down,
Which is the way to London Town?
Where? Where?
Up in the air,
Close your eyes and now you are there!

Soon, soon,
Afternoon,
Over the sunset, over the moon;
Far, far,
Over all bar,
Sweeping on from star to star!

No, no,
Low, low,
Sweeping daisies with my toe.
Slow, slow,
To and fro,
Slow—slow—slow—slow.

Algy

AUTHOR UNKNOWN

Algy met a bear,
The bear was bulgy,
The bulge was Algy.

31

Tired Tim

WALTER DE LA MARE

Poor tired Tim! It's sad for him.
He lags the long bright morning through,
Ever so tired of nothing to do,
He moons and mopes the livelong day,
Nothing to think about, nothing to say;
Up to bed with his candle to creep,
Too tired to yawn, too tired to sleep:
Poor tired Tim! It's sad for him.

The Chickens

AUTHOR UNKNOWN

Said the first little chicken,
    With a queer little squirm,
"I wish I could find
    A fat little worm."

Said the next little chicken,
    With an odd little shrug,
"I wish I could find
    A fat little slug."

Said the third little chicken,
    With a sharp little squeal,
"I wish I could find
    Some nice yellow meal."

Said the fourth little chicken,
    With a small sigh of grief,

"I wish I could find
  A little green leaf."

Said the fifth little chicken,
  With a faint little moan,
"I wish I could find
  A wee gravel stone."

"Now, see here," said the mother,
  From the green garden patch,
"If you want any breakfast,
  Just come here and scratch."

Adventures of Isabel

OGDEN NASH

Isabel met an enormous bear,
Isabel, Isabel, didn't care.
The bear was hungry, the bear was ravenous,
The bear's big mouth was cruel and cavernous.
The bear said, Isabel, glad to meet you,
How do, Isabel, now I'll eat you!
Isabel, Isabel, didn't worry;
Isabel didn't scream or scurry.
She washed her hands and she straightened her hair up,
Then Isabel quietly ate the bear up.

Once in a night as black as pitch
Isabel met a wicked old witch.
The witch's face was cross and wrinkled,
The witch's gums with teeth were sprinkled.
Ho, ho, Isabel! the old witch crowed,
I'll turn you into an ugly toad!
Isabel, Isabel, didn't worry;

33

Isabel didn't scream or scurry.
She showed no rage and she showed no rancor,
But she turned the witch into milk and drank her.

Isabel met a hideous giant,
Isabel continued self-reliant.
The giant was hairy, the giant was horrid,
He had one eye in the middle of his forehead.
Good morning Isabel, the giant said,
I'll grind your bones to make my bread.
Isabel, Isabel, didn't worry;
Isabel didn't scream or scurry.
She nibbled the zwieback that she always fed off,
And when it was gone, she cut the giant's head off.

Isabel met a troublesome doctor,
He punched and he poked till he really shocked her.
The doctor's talk was of coughs and chills,
And the doctor's satchel bulged with pills.
The doctor said unto Isabel,
Swallow this, it will make you well.
Isabel, Isabel, didn't worry;
Isabel didn't scream or scurry.
She took those pills from the pill-concocter,
And Isabel calmly cured the doctor.

I Do Not Love Thee, Doctor Fell

THOMAS BROWN

I do not love thee, Doctor Fell,
The reason why I cannot tell;
But this I know, and know full well,
I do not love thee, Doctor Fell.

Kitty

E. PRENTISS

Once there was a little kitty
    Whiter than snow;
In a barn she used to frolic,
    Long time ago.

In the barn a little mousie
    Ran to and fro;
For she heard the kitty coming,
    Long time ago.

Two eyes had little kitty,
    Black as a sloe;
And they spied the little mousie,
    Long time ago.

Four paws had little kitty,
    Paws soft as dough,
And they caught the little mousie,
    Long time ago.

Nine teeth had little kitty,
    All in a row;
And they bit the little mousie,
    Long time ago.

When the teeth bit little mousie,
    Little mouse cried "Oh!"
But she got away from kitty,
    Long time ago.

Holding Hands

LENORE M. LINK

Elephants walking
Along the trails

Are holding hands
By holding tails.

Trunks and tails
Are handy things

When elephants walk
In Circus rings.

Elephants work
And elephants play

And elephants walk
And feel so gay.

And when they walk—
It never fails

They're holding hands
By holding tails.

Five Little Sisters Walking in a Row

KATE GREENAWAY

Five little sisters walking in a row;
Now, isn't that the best way for little girls to go?
Each had a round hat, each had a muff,
And each had a new pelisse of soft green stuff.

Five little marigolds standing in a row;
Now, isn't that the best way for marigolds to grow?
Each with a green stalk, and all the five had got
A bright yellow flower and a new red pot.

The Drummer-Boy and the Shepherdess

WILLIAM BRIGHTLY RANDS

Drummer-boy, drummer-boy, where is your drum?
And why do you weep, sitting here on your thumb?
The soldiers are out, and the fifes we can hear;
But where is the drum of the young grenadier?

"My dear little drum it was stolen away
Whilst I was asleep on a sunshiny day;
It was all through the drone of a big bumble-bee,
And sheep and a shepherdess under a tree."

Shepherdess, shepherdess, where is your crook?
And why is your little lamb over the brook?
It bleats for its dam and dog Tray is not by,
So why do you stand with a tear in your eye?

"My dear little crook it was stolen away
Whilst I dreamt a dream on a morning in May;
It was all through the drone of a big bumble-bee
And a drum and a drummer boy under a tree."

Of Tact

ARTHUR GUITERMAN

Don't tell your friends about your indigestion:
"How are you!" is a greeting, not a question.

Bobby's First Poem

NORMAN GALE

It rely is ridikkelus
how uncle Charley tikkles us
at eester and at mikklemus
upon the nursry floor.

and rubbs our chins and bites our ears
like firty-fousand poler bares
and roars like lyons down the stares
and won't play enny more.

I Saw a Ship A-sailing

OLD RHYME

I saw a ship a-sailing,
A-sailing on the sea;
And, oh, it was all laden
With pretty things for thee.
There were comfits in the cabin,
And apples in the hold;
The sails were made of satin,
The masts were made of gold.
The four-and-twenty sailors
That stood between the decks,
Were four-and-twenty white mice
With chains about their necks.
The Captain was a duck, a duck,
With a jacket on his back;
And when the ship began to move
The Captain said, "Quack, quack."

Animal Fair

OLD RHYME

I went to the animal fair,
The birds and beasts were there.
The big baboon by the light of the moon
Was combing his auburn hair.

The monkey he got drunk.
He stepped on the elephant's trunk.
The elephant sneezed
And fell on his knees,
And that was the end of the munk, the munk, the munk.
And that was the end of the munk.

Git Along, Little Dogies

JOHN A. AND ALAN LOMAX

As I walked out one morning for pleasure
I spied a cowpuncher a-ridin' alone;
His hat was throwed back and his spurs was a-jinglin',
As he approached me a-singin' this song:

    Whoopee ti yi yo, git along, little dogies,
    It's your misfortune, and none of my own.
    Whoopee ti yi yo, git along, little dogies,
    For you know Wyoming will be your new home.

Early in the spring we round up the dogies,
Mark 'em and brand 'em and bob off their tails;
Round up our horses, load up the chuck-wagon,
Then throw the dogies upon the old trail.

It's whooping and yelling and driving the dogies;
Oh, how I wish you would go on!
It's whooping and punching and "Go on, little dogies,
For you know Wyoming will be your new home."

Some boys goes up the trail for pleasure,
But that's where you get it most awfully wrong;
For you haven't any idea the trouble they give us
While we go driving them all along.

When the night comes on and we hold them on the bed-
    ground,
These little dogies that roll on so slow;
Roll up the herd and cut out the strays,
And roll the little dogies that never rolled before.

Your mother she was raised way down in Texas,
Where the jimson weed and the sandburs grow;
Now we'll fill you up on prickly pear and cholla
Till you are ready for the trail to Idaho.

Oh, you'll be soup for Uncle Sam's Injuns,—
It's "beef, heap beef," I hear them cry.
Git along, git along, git along, little dogies,
You're going to be beef steers by and by.

> *Whoopee ti yi yo, git along, little dogies,*
> *It's your misfortune, and none of my own.*
> *Whoopee ti yi yo, git along, little dogies,*
> *For you know Wyoming will be your new home.*

A Roundabout Turn

ROBERT E. CHARLES

A Toad that lived on Albury Heath
Wanted to see the World.

"It isn't that I dislike the Heath,
It's a perfectly charming Heath, of course—

"All this heather, and all this gorse,
All this bracken to walk beneath,
With its feathery fronds to the sky uncurled—
It's as jolly a Heath as ever was found,

"But it's flat, and the World, they say, is round.
Yes, fancy," he said, "it's round, they tell me,
And wouldn't I like to go and see!

"But there—it's a long way down the road
For a fellow that walks as slow as a Toad.

"If I had a horse, I'd go," said he,
"If only I had a horse!
Who's got a horse," he cried, "to sell me?"

Well, nobody had, you see.

But horses came to the Heath one day,
Mettlesome steeds in brave array,
With prancing legs and staring eyes,
And crimson saddles that fall and rise
As round the galloping squadron flies,
And tents, and swings, and cokernut shies,
And a hoop-la stall with many a prize,
And races, and a band, and cheering.

41

"Hark!" said the Toad, "what's this I'm hearing?
It must be the World arrived, by the sound;
Now I'll see if it's really round!"

Off he crawled to the thick of things,
And the crowds made crawling rather tiring.
"Dear me," he said, "I wish I'd wings!
If this is the World," said he, perspiring,

"It's inconveniently full of Feet."

When a sudden voice said, "Look—how sweet!
Mummy, a toad! Let's give him a treat.

"It's not very safe for him on the ground,
So I'll put him up—

—on the merry-go-round."

And before the Toad could answer the floor began to slide,
The horses started prancing, and the riders settled to ride,
And they all moved faster, and the band began to play,
And away round he went with them, away and away and away.
Hooray! . . . .

So the Toad rode the Roundabout
Round and round and round;
No one minded him, he sat without a sound;
He rather liked the movement, he rather liked the tune,
      He just rode the Roundabout
All the afternoon.

When the time to pay came
What did he do?
"Tuppence a ride! Tuppence a ride! How much for you?"

42

Some had ridden for one ride, some had ridden for two—
   "Seventy-nine," the Toad cried;
The Boy said, "Coo!"

"But never you mind," the Toad replied,
"Here's an I.O.U."

"And now," he said, "I'll go, thanks,
I want to get home for tea.

"Another for nothing? NO, thanks,
"*Not* any more for me."

Home, holding the grasses,
Crawling a crooked road,

Slowly there passes

A very unsteady

Toad.

"Well, and what have you found, dear?
And what have you seen and heard?

"Is the World really round, dear?"
   "Round?" he said. "My word!
Round?"* said he; "you should feel it spin!
Roundest place I ever was in!
   Round!" he chuckled; "it's that!
But it's rather," he said with a knowing wink—
"It's rather a *giddy* place, I think.

"Give me a drop of the dew to drink,
     And give me the Heath; it's flat!"

Ballroom Dancing Class

PHYLLIS MCGINLEY

The little girls' frocks are frilly.
    The little boys' suits are blue.
On little gold chairs
They perch in pairs
    Awaiting their Friday cue.
The little boys stamp like ponies.
    The little girls coo like doves.
The little boys pummel their cronies
    With white, enormous gloves.
And overhead from a balcony
The twittering mothers crane to see.

Though sleek the curls
Of the little girls,
    Tossing their locks like foam,
Each little boy's tie
Has slipped awry
    And his hair forgets the comb.
He harks to the tuning fiddle
    With supercilious sneers.
His voice is cracked in the middle,
    Peculiar are his ears.
And little girls' mothers nod with poise
To distracted mothers of little boys.

Curtsying to the hostess,
    The little girls dip in line.
But hobbledehoy
Bobs each little boy,
    And a ramrod is his spine.
With little girls' charms prevailing,
    Why, as the music starts,

Are the little girls' mothers paling?
    And why do they clasp their hearts
When the hostess says with an arching glance,
"Let boys chose partners before we dance"?
Now little girls sway
Like buds in May
    And tremble upon the stalk.
But little boys wear
An arrogant air
    And they swagger when they walk.
The meagerest boy grows taller.
    The shyest one's done with doubt,
As he fingers a manful collar
    And singles his charmer out,
Or rakes the circle with narrowed eyes
To chose his suitable Friday prize.
While overhead in the balcony
The little boys' mothers smile to see
On razorless cheek and beardless chin
The Lord-of-Creation look begin.
Oh, little boys beckon, little girls bend!
And little boys' mothers condescend
(As they straighten their furs and pat their pearls)
To nod to the mothers of the little girls.

The Tutor

CAROLYN WELLS

A tutor who tootled the flute
    Was teaching two tooters to toot.
Said the two to the tutor,
    "Is it harder to toot,
Or to tutor two tooters to toot?"

45

The Height of the Ridiculous

OLIVER WENDELL HOLMES

I wrote some lines once on a time
    In wondrous merry mood,
And thought, as usual, men would say
    They were exceeding good.

They were so queer, so very queer,
    I laughed as I would die;
Albeit, in the general way,
    A sober man am I.

I called my servant, and he came;
    How kind it was of him
To mind a slender man like me,
    He of the mighty limb!

"These to the printer," I exclaimed,
    And, in my humorous way,
I added (as a trifling jest),
    "There'll be the devil to pay."

He took the paper, and I watched,
    And saw him peep within;
At the first line he read, his face
    Was all upon the grin.

He read the next; the grin grew broad,
    And shot from ear to ear;
He read the third; a chuckling noise
    I now began to hear.

The fourth; he broke into a roar;
    The fifth; his waistband split;

The sixth; he burst five buttons off,
　　And tumbled in a fit.

Ten days and nights, with sleepless eye,
　　I watched that wretched man,
And since, I never dare to write
　　As funny as I can.

Limericks

EDWARD LEAR

There was an Old Man in a pew,
Whose waistcoat was spotted with blue;
But he tore it in pieces, to give to his nieces,
That cheerful Old Man in a pew.

o

There was a Young Lady of Hull,
Who was chased by a virulent Bull;
But she seized on a spade, and called out—"Who's afraid!"
Which distracted that virulent Bull.

o

There was an Old Man of the Coast,
Who placidly sat on a post;
But when it was cold, he relinquished his hold,
And called for some hot buttered toast.

o

There was a Young Lady of Russia,
Who screamed so that no one could hush her;
Her screams were extreme, no one heard such a scream,
As was screamed by that Lady of Russia.

47

There was an old person of Dean
Who dined on one pea, and one bean;
For he said, "More than that, would make me too fat,"
That cautious old person of Dean.

Pussy and the Mice

OLD RHYME

Three little mice sat down to spin,
Pussy came by and she looked in.
"What are you at, my little men?"
"Making fine coats for gentlemen."

"May I come in and bite off your threads?"
"Oh, no, Miss Pussy, you'd bite off our heads."
"Oh, no, I'll not, I'll teach you to spin."
"That may be so, but you can't come in."

2
BLUM, BLUM, BLUM

Blum

DOROTHY ALDIS

Dog means dog,
And cat means cat;
And there are lots
Of words like that.

A cart's a cart
To pull or shove,
A plate's a plate,
To eat off of.

But there are other
Words I say
When I am left
Alone to play.

Blum is one.
Blum is a word
That very few
Have ever heard.

I like to say it,
"Blum, Blum, Blum"—
I do it loud
Or in a hum.

All by itself
It's nice to sing:
It does not mean
A single thing.

Merry Are the Bells

OLD RHYME

Merry are the bells, and merry would they ring,
Merry was myself, and merry could I sing;
With a merry ding-dong, happy, gay, and free,
And a merry sing-song, happy let us be!

Waddle goes your gait, and hollow are your hose;
Noddle goes your pate, and purple is your nose;
Merry is your sing-song, happy, gay, and free;
With a merry ding-dong, happy let us be!

51

Merry have we met, and merry have we been;
Merry let us part, and merry meet again;
With our merry sing-song, happy, gay, and free,
With a merry ding-dong, happy let us be!

Antonio

LAURA E. RICHARDS

Antonio, Antonio,
Was tired of living alonio.
    He thought he would woo
    Miss Lissamy Lou,
Miss Lissamy Lucy Molonio.

Antonio, Antonio,
Rode off on his polo-ponio.
    He found the fair maid
    In a bowery shade,
A-sitting and knitting alonio.

Antonio, Antonio,
Said, "If you will be my ownio,
    I'll love you true,
    And I'll buy for you,
An icery creamery conio!"

"Oh, nonio, Antonio!
You're far too bleak and bonio!
    And all that I wish,
    You singular fish,
Is that you will quickly begonio."

Antonio, Antonio,
He uttered a dismal moanio;
   Then ran off and hid
   (Or I'm told that he did)
In the Antarctical Zonio.

The Three Foxes

A. A. MILNE

Once upon a time there were three little foxes
Who didn't wear stockings, and they didn't wear sockses,
But they all had handkerchiefs to blow their noses,
And they kept their handkerchiefs in cardboard boxes.

They lived in the forest in three little houses,
And they didn't wear coats, and they didn't wear trousies.
They ran through the woods on their little bare tootsies,
And they played "Touch last" with a family of mouses.

They didn't go shopping in the High Street shopses,
But caught what they wanted in the woods and copses.
They all went fishing, and they caught three wormses,
They went out hunting and they caught three wopses.

They went to a Fair, and they all won prizes—
Three plum-puddingses and three mince-pieses.
They rode on elephants and swang on swingses,
And hit three coco-nuts at coco-nut shieses.

That's all that I know of the three little foxes
Who kept their handkerchiefs in cardboard boxes,
They lived in the forest in three little houses,
But they didn't wear coats and they didn't wear trousies,
And they didn't wear stockings and they didn't wear sockses.

The Great Panjandrum Himself

SAMUEL FOOTE

So she went into the garden
to cut a cabbage-leaf
to make an apple-pie;
and at the same time
a great she-bear, coming down the street,
pops its head into the shop.
What! no soap?
So he died,
and she very imprudently married the Barber.
And there were present
the Picninnies,
and the Joblillies,
and the Garyulies,
and the great Panjandrum himself,
with the little round button at top;
and they all fell to playing the game
of catch-as-catch-can,
till the gunpowder ran out at the heels of their boots.

The Frog

AUTHOR UNKNOWN

What a wonderful bird the frog are—
When he stand he sit almost;
When he hop, he fly almost.
He ain't got no sense hardly;
He ain't got no tail hardly either.
When he sit, he sit on what he ain't got almost.

54

Draw a Pail of Water

OLD RHYME

Draw a pail of water
For my Lady's daughter.
Father's a King,
Mother's a Queen,
My two little sisters are dressed in green,
Stamping marigolds and parsley.

The Mocking Fairy

WALTER DE LA MARE

"Won't you look out of your window, Mrs. Gill?"
Quoth the Fairy, nidding, nodding in the garden;
"Can't you look out of your window, Mrs. Gill?"
Quoth the Fairy, laughing softly in the garden;
But the air was still, the cherry boughs were still,
And the ivy-tod 'neath the empty sill,
And never from her window looked out Mrs. Gill
On the Fairy shrilly mocking in the garden.

"What have they done with you, you poor Mrs. Gill?"
Quoth the Fairy, brightly glancing in the garden;
"Where have they hidden you, you poor old Mrs. Gill?"
Quoth the Fairy dancing lightly in the garden;
But night's faint veil now wrapped the hill,
Stark 'neath the stars stood the dead-still Mill,
And out of her cold cottage never answered Mrs. Gill
The Fairy mimbling mambling in the garden.

55

Ring-A-Ring

KATE GREENAWAY

Ring-a-ring of little boys,
    Ring-a-ring of girls;
All around—all around,
    Twists and twirls.

You are merry children.
    "Yes, we are."
Where do you come from?
    "Not very far.

"We live in the mountain,
    We live in the tree;
And I live in the river bed
    And you won't catch me!"

The Nut Tree

OLD RHYME

I had a little nut tree,
Nothing would it bear,
But a silver nutmeg
And a golden pear.
The King of Spain's daughter
Came to visit me,
And all was because of
My little nut tree.
I skipped over water
I danced over sea,
And all the birds in the air
Could not catch me.

Counting-out Rhyme

EDNA ST. VINCENT MILLAY

Silver bark of beech, and sallow
Bark of yellow birch and yellow
Twig of willow.

Stripe of green in moosewood maple,
Color seen in leaf of apple,
Bark of popple.

Wood of popple pale as moonbeam,
Wood of oak for yoke and barn beam,
Wood of hornbeam.

Silver bark of beech, and hollow
Stem of elder, tall and yellow
Twig of willow.

The Owl and the Pussy-Cat

EDWARD LEAR

The Owl and the Pussy-Cat went to sea
    In a beautiful pea-green boat,
They took some honey, and plenty of money
    Wrapped up in a five-pound note.
The Owl looked up to the stars above,
    And sang to a small guitar,
"O lovely Pussy! O Pussy, my love,
    What a beautiful Pussy you are,
        You are,
        You are!
    What a beautiful Pussy you are!"

Pussy said to the Owl, "You elegant fowl!
    How charmingly sweet you sing!
O let us be married! too long we have tarried:
    But what shall we do for a ring?"
They sailed away for a year and a day,
    To the land where the Bong-tree grows,
And there in a wood a Piggy-wig stood,
    With a ring at the end of his nose,
        His nose,
        His nose,
    With a ring at the end of his nose.

"Dear Pig, are you willing to sell for one shilling
    Your ring?" Said the Piggy, "I will."
So they took it away, and were married next day
    By the Turkey who lives on the hill.
They dined on mince, and slices of quince,
    Which they ate with a runcible spoon;
And hand in hand, on the edge of the sand,
    They danced by the light of the moon,
        The moon,
        The moon,
    They danced by the light of the moon.

I Asked My Mother

I asked my mother for fifty cents
To see the elephant jump the fence.
He jumped so high that he touched the sky
And never came back till the Fourth of July.

58

If I Should Ever by Chance

EDWARD THOMAS

If I should ever by chance grow rich
I'll buy Codham, Cockridden, and Childerditch,
Roses, Pyrgo, and Lapwater,
And let them all to my elder daughter.
The rent I shall ask of her will be only
Each year's first violets, white and lonely,
The first primroses and orchises—
She must find them before I do, that is.
But if she finds a blossom on furze
Without rent they shall all forever be hers,
Codham, Cockridden, and Childerditch,
Roses, Pyrgo, and Lapwater,—
I shall give them all to my elder daughter.

Full Moon

V. SACKVILLE-WEST

She was wearing the coral taffeta trousers
Someone had brought her from Ispahan,
And the little gold coat with pomegranate blossoms,
And the coral-hafted feather fan;
But she ran down a Kentish lane in the moonlight,
And skipped in the pool of the moon as she ran.

She cared not a rap for all the big planets,
For Betelgeuse or Aldebaran,
And all the big planets cared nothing for her,
That small impertinent charlatan;
But she climbed on a Kentish stile in the moonlight,
And laughed at the sky through the sticks of her fan.

59

The Lobster Quadrille

LEWIS CARROLL

"Will you walk a little faster?" said the whiting to the snail,
"There's a porpoise close behind me, and he's treading on
     my tail.
See how eagerly the lobsters and the turtles all advance!
They are waiting on the shingle—will you come and join the
     dance?
Will you, won't you, will you, won't you, won't you join the
     dance?

"You can really have no notion how delightful it will be
When they take us up and throw us, with the lobsters, out
     to sea!"
But the snail replied, "Too far, too far!" and gave a look
     askance—
Said he thanked the whiting kindly, but he would not join
     the dance.
Would not, could not, would not, could not, would not join
     the dance.

"What matters it how far we go?" his scaly friend replied,
"There is another shore, you know, upon the other side.
The further off from England the nearer is to France—
Then turn not pale, beloved snail, but come and join the
     dance.
Will you, won't you, will you, won't you, will you join the
     dance?
Will you, won't you, will you, won't you, won't you join the
     dance?"

Miss James

A. A. MILNE

Diana Fitzpatrick Mauleverer James
Was lucky to have the most beautiful names.
How awful for fathers and mothers to call
Their children Jemima!—or nothing at all!
But *hers* were much wiser and kinder and cleverer,
They called her Diana Fitzpatrick Mauleverer James.

The Great Auk's Ghost

RALPH HODGSON

The Great Auk's ghost rose on one leg,
Sighed thrice and three times winkt,
And turned and poached a phantom egg
And muttered, "I'm extinct."

61

On a Night of Snow

ELIZABETH COATSWORTH

Cat, if you go outdoors you must walk in the snow.
You will come back with little white shoes on your feet,
Little white slippers of snow that have heels of sleet.
Stay by the fire, my Cat. Lie still, do not go.
See how the flames are leaping and hissing low,
I will bring you a saucer of milk like a marguerite,
So white and so smooth, so spherical and so sweet—
Stay with me, Cat. Outdoors the wild winds blow.

Outdoors the wild winds blow, Mistress, and dark is the night.
Strange voices cry in the trees, intoning strange lore,
And more than cats move, lit by our eyes' green light,
On silent feet where the meadow grasses hang hoar—
Mistress, there are portents abroad of magic and might,
And things that are yet to be done. Open the door!

Will You Be My Little Wife

KATE GREENAWAY

Will you be my little wife,
If I ask you? Do!
I'll buy you such a Sunday frock,
A nice umbrella, too.
And you shall have a little hat,
With such a long white feather,
A pair of gloves, and sandal shoes,
The softest kind of leather.
And you shall have a tiny house,
A beehive full of bees,
A little cow, a largish cat,
And green sage cheese.

62

Portrait by a Neighbor

EDNA ST. VINCENT MILLAY

Before she has her floor swept
    Or her dishes done,
Any day you'll find her
    A-sunning in the sun!

It's long after midnight
    Her key's in the lock,
And you never see her chimney smoke
    Till past ten o'clock!

She digs in her garden
    With a shovel and a spoon,
She weeds her lazy lettuce
    By the light of the moon,

She walks up the walk
    Like a woman in a dream,
She forgets she borrowed butter
    And pays you back cream!

Her lawn looks like a meadow,
    And if she mows the place
She leaves the clover standing
    And the Queen Anne's lace!

Tarantella

HILAIRE BELLOC

Do you remember an Inn, Miranda?
Do you remember an Inn?
And the tedding and the spreading

63

Of the straw for a bedding,
And the fleas that tease in the High Pyrenees,
And the wine that tasted of the tar?
And the cheers and the jeers of the young muleteers
(Under the vine of the dark verandah)?
Do you remember an Inn, Miranda,
Do you remember an Inn?
And the cheers and the jeers of, the young muleteers
Who hadn't got a penny,
And who weren't paying any,
And the hammer at the doors and the din?
And the *hip! hop! hap!*
Of the clap
Of the hands to the twirl and the swirl
Of the girl gone chancing,
Glancing,
Dancing,
Backing and advancing,
Snapping of the clapper to the spin
Out and in—
And the *ting, tong, tang* of the guitar!
Do you remember an Inn, Miranda?
Do you remember an Inn?

Never more; Miranda,
Never more.
Only the high peaks hoar:
And Aragon torrent at the door.
No sound
In the walls of the halls where falls
The tread
Of the feet of the dead to the ground,
No sound:
But the boom
Of the far waterfall like doom.

64

Overheard on a Saltmarsh

HAROLD MONRO

Nymph, nymph, what are your beads?
    Green glass, goblin. Why do you stare at them?

Give them me.

      No.

Give them me. Give them me.

        No.

Then I will howl all night in the reeds,
Lie in the mud and howl for them.

Goblin, why do you love them so?

They are better than stars or water,
Better than voices of winds that sing,
Better than any man's fair daughter,
Your green glass beads on a silver ring.

Hush, I stole them out of the moon.

Give me your beads, I desire them.

        No.

I will howl in a deep lagoon
For your green glass beads, I love them so.
Give them me. Give them.

      No.

Henry Was a Worthy King

OLD RHYME

Henry was a worthy King,
Mary was his Queen,
He gave her a lily
Upon a stalk of green.

Then all for his kindness,
And all for his care,
She gave him a new-laid egg
In the garden there.

Love, can you sing?
                    I cannot sing.
        Or story tell?
                    Not one I know.
Then let us play at Queen and King
        As down the garden walks we go.

Puck's Song

WILLIAM SHAKESPEARE

Now the hungry lion roars,
        And the wolf behowls the moon;
Whilst the heavy ploughman snores,
        All with weary task fordone.
Now the wasted brands do glow,
        Whilst the scritch-owl, scritching loud,
Puts the wretch that lies in woe
        In remembrance of a shroud.
Now it is the time of night,
        That the graves, all gaping wide,

66

Everyone lets forth his sprite,
    In the church-way paths to glide:
And we fairies, that do run
    By the triple Hecate's team,
From the presence of the sun,
    Following darkness like a dream,
Now are frolic; not a mouse
Shall disturb this hallow'd house:
I am sent with broom before
To sweep the dust behind the door.

Gentle Name

SELMA ROBINSON

Mary is a gentle name
Like the sound of silver bells,
Like a blue and quiet flame,
Like country brooks and ferny smells;
A friendly, wistful name and airy—
Mary.

A Grace

OLD RHYME

God bless the master of this house
    The mistress also,
And all the little children
    That round the table go,
And all your kin and kinsmen
    That dwell both far and near;
I wish you a Merry Christmas
    And a Happy New Year.

Little Orphant Annie

JAMES WHITCOMB RILEY

Little Orphant Annie comes to our house to stay,
An' wash the cups and saucers up, an' brush the crumbs
    away,
An' shoo the chickens off the porch, an' dust the hearth, an'
    sweep,
An' make the fire, an' bake the bread, an' earn her
    board-an'-keep;
An' all us other children, when the supper things is done,
We set around the kitchen fire an' has the mostest fun
A-list'nin' to the witch-tales 'at Annie tells about,
An' the Gobble-uns 'at gits you
        Ef you
           Don't
               Watch
                 Out!

Onc't they was a little boy wouldn't say his pray'rs—
An' when he went to bed at night, away up-stairs,
His mammy heerd him holler, an' his daddy heerd him bawl,
An' when they turned the kivvers down, he wasn't
    there at all!
An' they seeked him in the rafter room, an' cubby-hole, an'
    press,
An' seeked him in the chimbly flue, an' ever'wheres I guess,
But all they ever found was thist his pants and round-about!
An' the Gobble-uns'll git you
        Ef you
           Don't
               Watch
                 Out!

An' one time a little girl 'ud allus laugh 'nd grin,
An' make fun of ever' one, 'an all her blood-an'-kin;
An' onc't when they was "company," an' ole folks was there,
She mocked 'em an' shocked 'um, an' said she didn't care!
An' thist as she kicked her heels, an' turn't to run an' hide,
They was two great big Black Things a-standin' by her side,
An' they snatched her through the ceilin' 'fore she knowed
    what she's about!
An' the Gobble-uns'll git you
    Ef you
        Don't
            Watch
                Out!

An' little Orphant Annie says, when the blaze is blue,
An' the lampwick sputters, an' the wind goes wee-oo!
An' you hear the crickets quit, an' the moon is gray,
An' the lightnin'-bugs in dew is all squenched away,—
You better mind yer parents, an' yer teacher fond an' dear,
An' churish them 'at loves you, an' dry the orphant's tear
An' he'p the pore an' needy ones 'at cluster all about,
Er the Gobble-uns'll git you
    Ef you
        Don't
            Watch
                Out!

Captain Kidd

AUTHOR UNKNOWN

Oh, my name was Robert Kidd, as I sailed, as I sailed,
Oh, my name was Robert Kidd, as I sailed;
My sinful footsteps slid; God's laws they did forbid;
But still wickedly I did, as I sailed.

I'd a Bible in my hand, when I sailed, when I sailed;
I'd a Bible in my hand, when I sailed;
I'd a Bible in my hand, by my father's great command
And I sunk it in the sand, when I sailed.

    I spied three ships of France, as I sailed, as I sailed;
    I spied three ships of France, as I sailed;
    I spied three ships of France; to them I did advance,
    And I took them all by chance, as I sailed.

I spied three ships of Spain, as I sailed, as I sailed;
I spied three ships of Spain, as I sailed;
I spied three ships of Spain; I fired on them amain,
Till most of them were slain, as I sailed.

    I murdered William Moore, as I sailed, as I sailed;
    I murdered William Moore, as I sailed;
    I murdered William Moore, and I left him in his gore,
    Not many leagues from shore, as I sailed.

I'd ninety bars of gold, as I sailed, as I sailed;
I'd ninety bars of gold, as I sailed;
I'd dollars, manifold, and riches uncontrolled
And by these I lost my soul, as I sailed.

Wind Song

CARL SANDBURG

Long ago I learned how to sleep,
In an old apple orchard where the wind swept by counting
       its money and throwing it away,
In a wind-gaunt orchard where the limbs forked out and lis-
       tened or never listened at all,

In a passel of trees where the branches trapped the wind into
   whistling, "Who, who are you?"
I slept with my head in an elbow on a summer afternoon and
   there I took a sleep lesson.
There I went away saying: I know why they sleep, I know
   how they trap the tricky winds.
Long ago I learned how to listen to the singing wind and
   how to forget and how to hear the deep whine,
Slapping and lapsing under the day blue and the night stars:
            Who, who are you?
            Who can ever forget
            listening to the wind go by
            counting its money
            and throwing it away?

To Be or Not To Be

AUTHOR UNKNOWN

I sometimes think I'd rather crow
And be a rooster than to roost
And be a crow. But I dunno.

A rooster he can roost also,
Which don't seem fair when crows can't crow.
Which may help, some. Still I dunno.

Crows should be glad of one thing, though;
Nobody thinks of eating crow,
While roosters they are good enough
For anyone unless they're tough.

There are lots of tough old roosters though,
And anyway a crow can't crow,
So mebby roosters stand more show.
It looks that way. But I dunno.

Lady Moon

RICHARD MONCKTON MILNES

Lady Moon, Lady Moon, where are you roving?
    "Over the sea."
Lady Moon, Lady Moon, whom are you loving?
    "All that love me."

Are you not tired with rolling, and never
    Resting to sleep?
Why look so pale and sad, as forever
    Wishing to weep?

"Ask me not this, little child, if you love me;
    You are too bold:
I must obey my dear Father above me,
    And do as I'm told."

Lady Moon, Lady Moon, where are you roving?
    "Over the sea."
Lady Moon, Lady Moon, whom are you loving?
    "All that love me."

The Owl

ALFRED TENNYSON

When cats run home and light is come,
    And dew is cold upon the ground,
And the far-off stream is dumb,
    And the whirring sail goes round,
    And the whirring sail goes round;
        Alone and warming his five wits,
        The white owl in the belfry sits.

72

When merry milkmaids click the latch.
And rarely smells the new-mown hay,
And the cock hath sung beneath the thatch
Twice or thrice his roundelay,
Twice or thrice his roundelay;
Alone and warming his five wits,
The white owl in the belfry sits.

The Robin's Song

C. LOVAT FRASER

God bless the field and bless the furrow,
Stream and branch and rabbit burrow,
Hill and stone and flower and tree,
From Bristol Town to Wetherby—
Bless the sun and bless the sleet,
Bless the lane and bless the street,
Bless the night and bless the day,
From Somerset and all the way
To the meadows of Cathay.
Bless the minnow, bless the whale,
Bless the rainbow and the hail,
Bless the nest and bless the leaf,
Bless the righteous and the thief,
Bless the wing and bless the fin,
Bless the air I travel in,
Bless the mill and bless the mouse,
Bless the miller's bricken house,
Bless the earth and bless the sea;
God bless you, and God bless me!

A Piper

SEUMAS O'SULLIVAN

A piper in the streets today
Set up, and tuned, and started to play,
And away, away, away on the tide
Of his music we started; on every side
Doors and windows were opened wide,
And men left down their work and came,
And women with petticoats colored like flame.
And little bare feet that were blue with cold,
Went dancing back to the age of gold,
And all the world went gay, went gay,
For half an hour in the street today.

Farewell to the Fairies

RICHARD CORBET

Farewell rewards and fairies,
　　Good housewives now may say,
For now foul sluts in dairies
　　Do fare as well as they.
And though they sweep their hearths no less
　　Than maids were wont to do,
Yet who of late, for cleanliness,
　　Finds sixpence in her shoe?

At morning and at evening both,
　　You merry were and glad,
So little care of sleep or sloth
　　Those pretty ladies had.
When Tom came home from labour,
　　Or Cis to milking rose,

74

Then merrily went their tabor,
    And nimbly went their toes.

Witness those rings and roundelays
    Of theirs, which yet remain,
Were footed in Queen Mary's days
    On many a grassy plain;
But since of late Elizabeth,
    And later, James came in,
They never danced on any heath
    As when the time hath been.

By which we note the fairies
    Were of the old profession,
Their songs were Ave-Maries,
    Their dances were procession:
But now, alas! they all are dead,
    Or gone beyond the seas;
Or farther for religion fled,
    Or else they take their ease.

A tell-tale in their company
    They never could endure,
And whoso kept not secretly
    Their mirth, was punished sure;
It was a just and Christian deed
    To pinch such black and blue:
O how the commonwealth doth need
    Such justices as you!

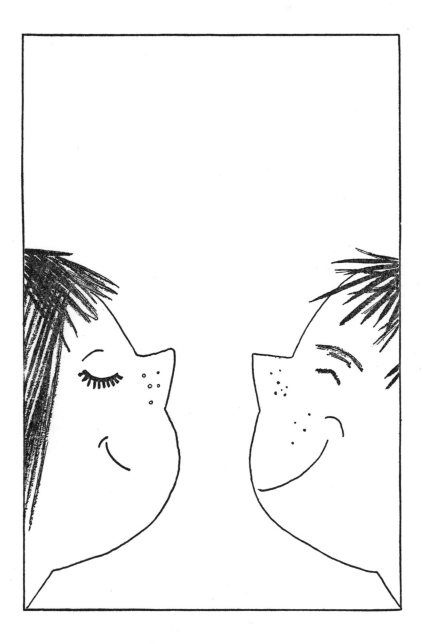

I Know Where I'm Going

AUTHOR UNKNOWN

I know where I'm going,
    I know who's going with me,
    I know who I love,
    But the dear knows who I'll marry.

    I'll have stockings of silk,
    Shoes of fine green leather,
    Combs to buckle my hair
    And a ring for every finger.

    Feather beds are soft,
    Painted rooms are bonny;
    But I'd leave them all
    To go with my love Johnny.

    Some say he's dark,
    I say he's bonny,
    He's the flower of them all,
    My handsome, coaxing Johnny.

    I know where I'm going,
    I know who's going with me,
    I know who I love,
    But the dear knows who I'll marry.

The Modern Hiawatha

GEORGE A. STRONG

He killed the noble Mudjokivis;
With the skin he made him mittens,
Made them with the fur side inside,

Made them with the skin side outside,
He, to get the warm side inside,
Put the inside skin side outside:
He, to get the cold side outside,
Put the warm side fur side inside:
That's why he put the fur side inside,
Why he put the skin side outside,
Why he turned them inside outside.

Charlie Chaplin Went to France
(A Jump Rope Rhyme)

CARL WITHERS

Charlie Chaplin went to France
To teach the ladies how to dance.
Heel, toe, and around we go;
Salute to the captain,
Bow to the queen,
Turn your back
On the old submarine.

Grace for a Child

ROBERT HERRICK

Here a little child I stand,
      Heaving up my either hand;
Cold as paddocks though they be,
      Here I lift them up to Thee,
For a benison to fall
      On our meat and on us all.
                              Amen

3
OVER IN THE MEADOW

Over in the Meadow

OLIVER A. WADSWORTH

Over in the meadow,
    In the sand, in the sun,
Lived an old mother toad
    And her little toadie one.
"Wink!" said the mother;
    "I wink," said the one:
So he winked and he blinked
    In the sand, in the sun.

Over in the meadow,
    Where the streams run blue,
Lived an old mother fish
    And her little fishes two.
"Swim!" said the mother;
    "We swim," said the two:
So they swam and they leaped
    Where the stream runs blue.

Over in the meadow,
    In a hole in a tree,
Lived a mother bluebird
    And her birdies three.
"Sing!" said the mother;
    "We sing," said the three:
So they sang and were glad
    In the hole in the tree.

Over in the meadow,
    In the reeds on the shore,
Lived a mother muskrat
    And her little ratties four.
"Dive," said the mother;
    "We dive," said the four:
So they dived and they burrowed
    In the weeds on the shore.

Over in a meadow,
    In a snug beehive,
Lived a mother honey-bee
    And her little honeys five.
"Buzz," said the mother;
    "We buzz," said the five:
So they buzzed and they hummed
    In the snug beehive.

Over in a meadow,
    In a nest built of sticks,
Lived a black mother crow
    And her little crows six.
"Caw," said the mother;
    "We caw," said the six:
So they cawed and they cawed
    In their nest built of sticks.

Over in a meadow,
    Where the grass is so even,
Lived a gray mother cricket
    And her little crickets seven.
"Chirp," said the mother;
    "We chirp," said the seven:
So they chirped cheery notes
    In the grass soft and even.

Over in the meadow,
    By the old mossy gate,
Lived a brown mother lizzard
    And her little lizzards eight.
"Bask," said the mother;
    "We bask," said the eight:
So they basked in the sun
    By the old mossy gate.

Over in the meadow,
    Where the clear pools shine,
Lived a green mother frog
    And her little froggies nine.
"Croak," said the mother;
    "We croak," said the nine.
So they croaked and they splashed
    Where the clear pools shine.

Over in the meadow,
    In a sly little den,
Lived a gray mother spider
    And her little spiders ten.
"Spin," said the mother;
    "We spin," said the ten:
So they spun lace webs
    In their sly little den.

Over in the meadow,
    In the soft summer even,
Lived a mother firefly
    And her little flies eleven.
"Shine," said the mother;
    "We shine," said the eleven:
So they shone like stars
    In the soft summer even.

Over in the meadow,
    Where the men dig and delve,
Lived a wise mother ant
    And her little anties twelve.
"Toil," said the mother;
    "We toil," said the twelve:
So they toiled and were wise,
    Where the men dig and delve.

Hie Away

WALTER SCOTT

Hie away, hie away
Over bank and over brae,
Where the copsewood is the greenest,
Where the fountains glisten sheenest,
Where the lady-fern grows strongest,
Where the morning dew lies longest,
Where the black-cock sweetest sips it,
Where the fairy latest trips it:
Hie to haunts right seldom seen,
Lovely, lonesome, cool, and green,
Over bank and over brae
Hie away, hie away.

White Fields

JAMES STEPHENS

I

In the winter time we go
Walking in the fields of snow;

Where there is no grass at all;
Where the top of every wall,

Every fence and every tree,
Is as white as white can be.

II

Pointing out the way we came,
—Every one of them the same—

All across the fields there be
Prints in silver filigree;

And our mothers always know,
By the footprints in the snow,
Where it is the children go.

A Bird Came Down the Walk

EMILY DICKINSON

A bird came down the walk:
He did not know I saw;
He bit an angleworm in halves
And ate the fellow, raw.

84

And then he drank a dew
From a convenient grass,
And then hopped sidewise to the wall
To let a beetle pass.

He glanced with rapid eyes
That hurried all abroad,—
They looked like frightened beads, I thought
He stirred his velvet head

Like one in danger; cautious,
I offered him a crumb,
And he unrolled his feathers
And rowed him softer home

Than oars divide the ocean,
Too silver for a seam,
Or butterflies, off banks of noon,
Leap, splashless, as they swim.

A Boy's Song

JAMES HOGG

Where the pools are bright and deep,
Where the grey trout lies asleep,
Up the river and over the lea,
That's the way for Billy and me.

Where the blackbird sings the latest,
Where the hawthorn blooms the sweetest,
Where the nestlings chirp and flee,
That's the way for Billy and me.

Where the mowers mow the cleanest,
Where the hay lies thick and greenest,
There to track the homeward bee,
That's the way for Billy and me.

Where the hazel bank is steepest,
Where the shadow lies the deepest,
Where the clustering nuts fall free,
That's the way for Billy and me.

This I know, I love to play,
Through the meadow, among the hay;
Up the water and over the lea,
That's the way for Billy and me.

The Wind in a Frolic

WILLIAM HOWITT

The wind one morning sprang up from sleep,
Saying, "Now for a frolic! now for a leap!
Now for a madcap galloping chase!
I'll make a commotion in every place!"
So it swept with a bustle right through a great town,
Creaking the signs and scattering down
Shutters; and whisking, with merciless squalls,
Old women's bonnets and gingerbread stalls.
There never was heard a much lustier shout,
As the apples and oranges trundled about;
And the urchins, that stand with their thievish eyes
For ever on watch, ran off each with a prize.
Then away to the field it went blustering and humming,
And the cattle all wondered whatever was coming.
It plucked by their tails the grave matronly cows,
And tossed the colts' manes all about their brows,

86

Till, offended at such a familiar salute,
They all turned their backs, and stood sullenly mute.
So on it went, capering and playing its pranks;
Whistling with reeds on the broad river's banks;
Puffing the birds as they sat on the spray,
Or the traveller grave on the king's highway.
It was not too nice to hustle the bags
Of the beggar, and flutter his dirty rags;
'Twas so bold that it feared not to play its joke
With the doctor's wig, or the gentleman's cloak.
Through the forest it roared, and cried gaily, "Now,
You sturdy old oaks, I'll make you bow!"
And it made them bow without more ado,
Or it cracked their great branches through and through.
Then it rushed like a monster on cottage and farm,
Striking their dwellers with sudden alarm;
And they ran out like bees in a midsummer swarm.
There were dames with their kerchiefs tied over their caps,
To see if their their poultry were free from mishaps;
The turkeys they gobbled, the geese screamed aloud,
And the hens crept to roost in a terrified crowd;
There was rearing of ladders, and logs laying on
Where the thatch from the roof threatened soon to be gone.
But the wind had passed on, and had met in a lane
With a schoolboy, who panted and struggled in vain;
For it tossed him and twirled him, then passed, and he stood
With his hat in a pool and his shoe in the mud.
But away went the wind in its holiday glee,
And now it was far on the billowy sea,
And the lordly ships felt its staggering blow,
And the little boats darted to and fro.
But lo! it was night, and it sank to rest,
On the sea-bird's rock in the gleaming West,
Laughing to think, in its fearful fun,
How little of mischief it had done.

Queen Anne's Lace

MARY LESLIE NEWTON

Queen Anne, Queen Anne, has washed her lace
    (She chose a summer day)
And hung it in a grassy place
    To whiten, if it may.

Queen Anne, Queen Anne, has left it there,
    And slept the dewy night;
Then waked, to find the sunshine fair,
    And all the meadows white.

Queen Anne, Queen Anne, is dead and gone
    (She died a summer's day),
But left her lace to whiten on
    Each weed-entangled way!

Millions of Strawberries

GENEVIEVE TAGGARD

Marcia and I went over the curve,
Eating our way down
Jewels of strawberries we didn't deserve,
Eating our way down.
Till our hands were sticky, and our lips painted,
And over us the hot day fainted,
And we saw snakes,
And got scratched,
And a lust overcame us for the red unmatched
Small buds of berries,
Till we lay down—
Eating our way down—

88

And rolled in the berries like two little dogs,
Rolled
In the late gold.
And gnats hummed,
And it was cold,
And home we went, home without a berry,
Painted red and brown,
Eating our way down.

Summer Evening

WALTER DE LA MARE

The sandy cat by the Farmer's chair
Mews at his knee for dainty fare;
Old Rover in his moss-greened house
Mumbles a bone, and barks at a mouse.
In the dewy fields the cattle lie
Chewing the cud 'neath a fading sky.
Dobbin at manger pulls his hay:
Gone is another summer's day.

Dust of Snow

ROBERT FROST

The way a crow
Shook down on me
The dust of snow
From a hemlock tree
Has given my heart
A change of mood,
And saved some part
Of a day I rued.

The River-God's Song

BEAUMONT AND FLETCHER

Do not fear to put thy feet
Naked in the river sweet;
Think not leech, or newt, or toad
Will bite thy foot when thou hast trod;
Nor let the water, rising high,
As thou wadest, make thee cry,
And sob; but ever live with me,
And not a wave shall trouble thee.

I'll Tell You How the Sun Rose

EMILY DICKINSON

I'll tell you how the sun rose,—
A ribbon at a time.
The steeples swam in amethyst,
The news like squirrels ran.

The hills untied their bonnets,
The bobolinks begun.
Then I said softly to myself,
"That must have been the sun!"

But how he set, I know not.
There seemed a purple stile
Which little yellow boys and girls
Were climbing all the while.

Till when they reached the other side,
A dominie in gray
Put gently up the evening bars,
And led the flock away.

To Nature Seekers

ROBERT W. CHAMBERS

Where the slanting forest eves
Shingled light with greenest leaves
Sweep the scented meadow sedge
Let us snoop along the edge,
Let us pry in hidden nooks
Laden with our nature books,
Scaring birds with happy cries,
Chloroforming butterflies,
Rooting up each woodland plant,
Pinning beetle, fly and ant
So we may identify
What we've ruined by and by.

Ducks' Ditty

KENNETH GRAHAME

All along the backwater,
Through the rushes tall,
Ducks are a-dabbling,
Up tails all!

Ducks' tails, drakes' tails,
Yellow feet a-quiver,
Yellow bills all out of sight
Busy in the river!

Slushy green undergrowth
Where the roach swim—
Here we keep our larder,
Cool and full and dim.

Everyone for what he likes!
We like to be
Heads down, tails up,
Dabbling free!

High in the blue above
Swifts whirl and call—
We are down a-dabbling
Up tails all!

The Field Mouse

WILLIAM SHARP

When the moon shines o'er the corn
And the beetle drones his horn,
And the flittermice swift fly,
And the nightjars swooping cry,
And the young hares run and leap,
We waken from our sleep.

And we climb with tiny feet
And we munch the green corn sweet
With startled eyes for fear
The white owl should fly near,
Or long slim weasel spring
Upon us where we swing.

We do not hurt at all;
Is there not room for all
Within the happy world?
All day we lie close curled
In drowsy sleep, nor rise
Till through the dusky skies
The moon shines o'er the corn
And the beetle drones his horn.

Psalm of Those Who Go Forth Before Daylight

CARL SANDBURG

The policeman buys shoes slow and careful; the teamster
    buys gloves slow and careful; they take care of their feet
    and hands; they live on their feet and hands.

The milkman never argues; he works alone and no one
    speaks to him; the city is asleep when he is on the job;
    he puts a bottle on six hundred porches and calls it a
    day's work; he climbs two hundred wooden stairways;
    two horses are company for him; he never argues.

The rolling mill-men and the sheet-steel men are brothers;
    of cinders, they empty cinders out of their shoes after
    the day's work; they ask their wives to fix burnt holes in
    the knees of their trousers; their necks and ears are cov-
    ered with a smut; they scour their necks and ears; they
    are brothers of cinders.

The Pasture

ROBERT FROST

I'm going out to clean the pasture spring;
I'll only stop to rake the leaves away
(And wait to watch the water clear, I may):
I shan't be gone long.—You come too.

I'm going out to fetch the little calf
That's standing by the mother. It's so young,
It totters when she licks it with her tongue.
I shan't be gone long.—You come too.

Chanson Innocent

E. E. CUMMINGS

in Just-
spring   when the world is mud-
luscious the little
lame baloonman

whistles   far   and wee
and eddieandbill come
running from marbles and
piracies and it's
spring

when the world is puddle-wonderful

the queer
old baloonman whistles
far   and   wee

and bettyandisbel come dancing
from hop-scotch and jump-rope and

it's
spring
and
      the
            goat-footed

baloonman   whistles
far
and
wee

Spring

WILLIAM BLAKE

Sound the flute!
Now it's mute.
Birds delight
Day and Night;
Nightingale
In the dale,
Lark in Sky,
Merrily,
Merrily, merrily, to welcome in the Year.

Little Boy,
Full of joy;
Little Girl,
Sweet and small;
Cock does crow,
So do you;
Merry voice,
Infant noise,
Merrily, merrily, to welcome in the Year.

Little Lamb,
Here I am;
Come and lick
My white neck;
Let me pull
Your soft Wool;
Let me kiss
Your soft face;
Merrily, merrily, to welcome in the Year.

Robin Redbreast

WILLIAM ALLINGHAM

Good-bye, good-bye to summer!
    For summer's nearly done;
The garden smiling faintly,
    Cool breezes in the sun;
Our thrushes now are silent,
    Our swallows flown away—
But Robin's here, in coat of brown,
    With ruddy breast-knot gay.
Robin, Robin Redbreast,
    O Robin dear!
Robin singing sweetly,
    In the falling of the year.

Bright yellow, red, and orange,
    The leaves come down in hosts;
The trees are Indian princes,
    But soon they'll turn to ghosts;
The scanty pears and apples
    Hang russet on the bough,
It's autumn, autumn, autumn late,
    'Twill soon be winter now.
Robin, Robin Redbreast,
    O Robin dear!
And welaway! my Robin,
    For pinching times are near.

The fireside for the cricket,
    The wheatstack for the mouse,
When trembling night-winds whistle
    And moan all round the house;
The frosty ways like iron,
    The branches plumed with snow—

Alas! in winter, dead and dark,
    Where can poor Robin go?
Robin, Robin Redbreast,
    O Robin dear!
And a crumb of bread for Robin,
    His little heart to cheer.

Evening on the Farm

JOHN TOWNSEND TROWBRIDGE

Over the hill the farm-boy goes.
His shadow lengthens along the land,
A giant staff in a giant hand;
In the poplar-tree, above the spring,
The katydids begin to sing;
    The early dews are falling.
Into the stone-heap darts the mink;
The swallow skims the river's brink;
And home to the woodland fly the crows,
When over the hill the farm-boy goes,
Cheerily calling,
    "Co' boss! co', boss! co'! co'! co'!"
Farther, farther, over the hill,
Faintly calling, calling still,
    "Co' boss! co' boss! co' co'!"

Into the yard the farmer goes,
With grateful heart, at the close of day;
Harness and chain are hung away;
In the wagon-shed stand yoke and plow,
The straw's in the stack, the hay in the mow
    The cooling dews are falling;
The friendly sheep his welcome bleat,
The pigs come grunting to his feet

97

And the whinnying mare her master knows,
When in the yard the farmer goes,
 His cattle calling,
  "Co' boss! co', boss! co'! co'! co'!"
While still the cow-boy, far away,
Goes seeking those that have gone astray,
  "Co' boss! co' boss! co' co'!"

Now to her task the milkmaid goes.
The cattle come crowding through the gate,
Lowing, pushing, little and great;
About the trough by the farmyard pump,
The frolicksome yearlings frisk and jump,
 While the pleasant dews are falling.
The new milch heifer is quick and shy,
But the old cow waits with tranquil eye,
And the white stream into the bright pail flows,
When to her task the milkmaid goes,
  Soothingly calling,
  "So, boss! so, boss! so! so! so!"

The cheerful milkmaid takes her stool,
And sits and milks in the twilight cool,
  Saying, "So! so, boss! so! so!"
To supper at last the farmer goes,
The apples are pared, the paper read,
The stories are told, then all to bed.
Without, the crickets' ceaseless song
Makes shrill the silence all night long;
 The heavy dews are falling.

The housewife's hand has turned the lock;
Drowsily ticks the kitchen clock;
The household sinks to deep repose,
But still in sleep the farm-boy goes

Singing, calling,
   "Co' boss! co', boss! co'! co'! co'!"
And oft the milkmaid, in her dreams,
Drums in the pail with the flashing streams,
   Murmuring "So, boss! so!"

The Green Grass Growing All Around

OLD RHYME

There was a tree stood in the ground,
The prettiest tree you ever did see;
The tree in the wood, and the wood in the ground,
And the green grass growing all around.
And the green grass growing all around.

And on this tree there was a limb,
The prettiest limb you ever did see;
The limb on the tree, and the tree in the wood,
The tree in the wood, and the wood in the ground,
And the green grass growing all around.
And the green grass growing all around.

And on this limb there was a bough,
The prettiest bough you ever did see;
The bough on the limb, and the limb on the tree,
The limb on the tree, and the tree in the wood,
The tree in the wood, and the wood in the ground,
And the green grass growing all around.
And the green grass growing all around.

Now on this bough there was a nest,
The prettiest nest you ever did see;
The nest on the bough, and the bough on the limb,
The bough on the limb, and the limb on the tree,

The limb on the tree, and the tree in the wood,
The tree in the wood, and the wood in the ground,
And the green grass growing all around.
And the green grass growing all around.

And in the nest there were some eggs,
The prettiest eggs you ever did see;
Eggs in the nest, and the nest on the bough,
The nest on the bough, and the bough on the limb,
The bough on the limb, and the limb on the tree,
The limb on the tree, and the tree in the wood,
The tree in the wood, and the wood in the ground,
And the green grass growing all around.
And the green grass growing all around.

Stopping by Woods on a Snowy Evening

ROBERT FROST

Whose woods these are I think I know.
His house is in the village though;
He will not see me stopping here
To watch his woods fill up with snow.

My little horse must think it queer
To stop without a farmhouse near
Between the woods and frozen lake
The darkest evening of the year.

He gives his harness bells a shake
To ask if there is some mistake.
The only other sound's the sweep
Of easy wind and downy flake.

The woods are lovely, dark and deep,
But I have promises to keep,
And miles to go before I sleep,
And miles to go before I sleep.

Leisure

WILLIAM HENRY DAVIES

What is this life if, full of care,
We have no time to stand and stare.

No time to stand beneath the boughs
And stare as long as sheep or cows.

No time to see, when woods we pass,
Where squirrels hide their nuts in grass.

No time to see, in broad daylight,
Streams full of stars like skies at night.

No time to turn at Beauty's glance,
And watch her feet, how they can dance.

No time to wait till her mouth can
Enrich the smile her eyes began.

A poor life this, is full of care,
We have no time to stand and stare.

The Merry Month of March

WILLIAM WORDSWORTH

The cock is crowing,
The stream is flowing,
The small birds twitter,
The lake doth glitter,
The green field sleeps in the sun;

The oldest and youngest
Are at work with the strongest;
The cattle are grazing,
Their heads never raising;
There are forty feeding like one!

Like an army defeated
The snow hath retreated,
And now doth fare ill
On the top of the bare hill;
The Plough-boy is whooping anon, anon.
There's joy in the mountains;
There's life in the fountains;
Small clouds are sailing,
Blue sky prevailing;
The rain is over and gone!

At the Dog Show
(To an Irish Wolfhound)

CHRISTOPHER MORLEY

Long and gray and gaunt he lies,
A Lincoln among dogs; his eyes,
Deep and clear of sight, appraise
The meaningless and shuffling ways
Of human folk that stop to stare.
One witless woman, seeing there
How tired, how contemptuous
He is of all the smell and fuss,
Asks him, "Poor fellow, are you sick?"

Yea, sick and weary to the quick
Of heat and noise from dawn to dark.
He will not even stoop to bark
His protest, like the lesser bred.

Would he might know, one gazer read
The wistful longing in his face,
The thirst for wind and open space
And stretch of limbs to him begrudged.

There came a little, dapper, fat
And bustling man, with cane and spat
And pearl-gray vest and derby hat—
Such were the judger and the judged!

The Duck

OGDEN NASH

Behold the duck.
It does not cluck.
A cluck it lacks.
It quacks.
It is specially fond
Of a puddle or pond.
When it dines or sups,
It bottoms ups.

The Falling Star

SARA TEASDALE

I saw a star slide down the sky,
Blinding the north as it went by,
Too burning and too quick to hold,
Too lovely to be bought or sold,
Good only to make wishes on
And then forever to be gone.

A Thought

WILLIAM HENRY DAVIES

When I look into a glass
    Myself's my only care;
But I look into a pool
    For all the wonders there.

When I look into a glass
    I see a fool;
But I see a wise man
    When I look into a pool.

Some One

WALTER DE LA MARE

Someone came knocking
    At my wee, small door;
Someone came knocking,
    I'm sure—sure—sure;
I listened, I opened,
    I looked to left and right,
But nought there was a-stirring
    In the still dark night;
Only the busy beetle
    Tap-tapping in the wall,
Only from the forest
    The screech-owl's call,
Only the cricket whistling
    While the dewdrops fall,
So I know not who came knocking,
    At all, at all, at all.

4

HOW MANY MILES TO BABYLON?

How Many Miles to Babylon?

OLD RHYME

How many miles to Babylon?
Three score and ten.
Can I get there by candlelight?
Yes, and back again.
Then open the gates wide
And let the king and his men come in.

106

Travel

ROBERT LOUIS STEVENSON

I should like to rise and go
Where the golden apples grow;
Where below another sky
Parrot islands anchored lie,
And, watched by cockatoos and goats,
Lonely Crusoes building boats;
Where in sunshine reaching out
Eastern cities, miles about,
Are with mosque and minaret
Among sandy gardens set,
And the rich goods from near and far
Hang for sale in the bazaar;
Where the Great Wall round China goes,
And on one side the desert blows,
And with bell and voice and drum,
Cities on the other hum;
Where are forests, hot as fire,
Wide as England, tall as a spire,
Full of apes and coconuts
And the Negro hunters' huts;
Where the knotty crocodile
Lies and blinks in the Nile,
And the red flamingo flies
Hunting fish before his eyes;
Where in jungles, near and far,
Man-devouring tigers are;
Lying close and giving ear
Lest the hunt be drawing near,
Or a comer-by be seen
Swinging in a palanquin;
Where among the desert sands
Some deserted city stands,

All its children, sweep and prince,
Grown to manhood ages since,
Not a foot in street or house,
Not a stir of child or mouse,
And when kindly falls the night,
In all the town no spark of light.
There I'll come when I'm a man
With a camel caravan;
Light a fire in the gloom
Of some dusty dining room;
See the pictures on the walls,
Heroes, fights and festivals;
And in a corner find the toys
Of the old Egyptian boys.

Travel

EDNA ST. VINCENT MILLAY

The railroad track is miles away,
    And the day is loud with voices speaking,
But there isn't a train goes by all day
    But I hear its whistle shrieking.

All night there isn't a train goes by
    Though the night is still for sleep and dreaming,
But I see its cinders red on the sky
    And hear its engine steaming.

My heart is warm with the friends I make,
    And better friends I'll not be knowing,
Yet there isn't a train I wouldn't take,
    No matter where it's going.

Rhyme of the Rail

J. G. SAXE

Singing through the forests, rattling over ridges,
Shooting under arches, rumbling over bridges,
Whizzing through the mountains, buzzing o'er the vale—
Bless me! this is pleasant, riding on the rail!

Men of different stations, in the eye of Fame,
Here are very quickly coming to the same;
High and lowly people, birds of every feather,
On a common level, travelling together!

Gentlemen in shorts, looming very tall;
Gentlemen at large, talking very small;
Gentlemen in tights with a loose-ish mien;
Gentlemen in grey, looking rather green;

Gentlemen quite old, asking for the news;
Gentlemen in black, in a fit of blues;
Gentlemen in claret, sober as a vicar;
Gentlemen in tweed, dreadfully in liquor!

Stranger on the right, looking very sunny,
Obviously reading something rather funny.
Now the smiles are thicker—wonder what they mean?
Sure, he's got the Knickerbocker Magazine!

Stranger on the left, closing up his peepers;
Now he snores amain, like the seven sleepers;
At his feet a volume gives the explanation,
How the man grew stupid from "association!"

Ancient maiden lady anxiously remarks
That there must be peril 'mong so many sparks:

Roguish-looking fellow, turning to the stranger,
Says it's his opinion, *she* is out of danger!

Woman with her baby, sitting *vis-a-vis*;
Baby keeps a-squalling, woman looks at me;
Asks about the distance; says it's tiresome talking,
Noises of the cars are so very shocking!

Market woman, careful of the precious casket,
Knowing eggs are eggs, tightly holds her basket;
Feeling that a smash, if it came, would surely
Send her eggs to pot, rather prematurely.

Singing through the forests, rattling over ridges,
Shooting under arches, rumbling over bridges,
Whizzing through the mountains, buzzing o'er the vale—
Bless me! this is pleasant, riding on the rail!

The Walloping Window Blind

CHARLES CARRYL

Oh, a capital ship for an ocean trip,
    Was the *Walloping Window Blind*;
No gale that blew dismayed her crew
    Or troubled the captain's mind.
The man at the wheel was taught to feel
    Contempt for the wildest blow,
And it often appeared, when the weather had cleared,
    That he'd been in his bunk below.

The boatswain's mate was very sedate,
    Yet fond of amusement, too;
And he played hopscotch with the starboard watch,
    While the captain tickled the crew.

And the gunner we had was apparently mad,
    For he sat on the after-rail,
And fired salutes with the captain's boots,
    In the teeth of the booming gale.

The captain sat in a commodore's hat
    And dined in a royal way
On toasted pigs and pickles and figs
    And gummery bread each day.
But the cook was Dutch, and behaved as such;
    For the diet he gave the crew
Was a number of tons of hot-cross buns
    Prepared with sugar and glue.

All nautical pride we laid aside,
    And we cast the vessel ashore
On the Gulliby Isles where the Pooh-pooh smiles,
    And the Rumbletum bunders roar.
And we sat on the edge of a sandy ledge
    And shot at the whistling bee;
And the cinnamon bats wore waterproof hats
    As they danced in the sounding sea.

On rubgub bark, from dawn to dark,
    We fed till we all had grown
Uncommonly shrunk—when a Chinese junk
    Came by from the torriby zone.
She was stubby and square, but we didn't much care,
    And we cheerily put to sea;
And we left the crew of the junk to chew
    The bark of the rubgub tree.

I Like to See It Lap the Miles

EMILY DICKINSON

I like to see it lap the miles,
And lick the valleys up,
And stop to feed itself at tanks;
And then, prodigious, step

Around a pile of mountains,
And, supercilious, peer
In shanties by the sides of roads;
And then a quarry pare

To fit its sides, and crawl between,
Complaining all the while
In horrid, hooting stanza;
Then chase itself down hill

And neigh like Boanerges;
Then, punctual as a star,
Stop—docile and omnipotent—
At its own stable door.

The Unexplorer

EDNA ST. VINCENT MILLAY

There was a road ran past our house
    Too lovely to explore.
I asked my mother once—she said
    That if you followed where it led
It brought you to the milk-man's door.
    (That's why I have not traveled more.)

112

The Good Joan

LIZETTE WOODWORTH REESE

Along the thousand roads of France,
Now there, now here, swift as a glance,
A cloud, a mist blown down the sky,
Good Joan of Arc goes riding by.

In Domremy at candlelight,
The orchards blowing rose and white
About the shadowy houses lie;
And Joan of Arc goes riding by.

On Avignon there falls a hush,
Brief as the singing of a thrush
Across old gardens April-high;
And Joan of Arc goes riding by.

The women bring the apples in,
Round Arles when the long gusts begin,
Then sit them down to sob and cry;
And Joan of Arc goes riding by.

Dim falls the hoofs down old Calais;
In Tours a flash of silver-gray,
Like flaw of rain in a clear sky;
And Joan of Arc goes riding by.

Who saith that ancient France shall fail,
A rotting leaf driv'n down the gale?
Then her sons know not how to die;
Then good God dwells no more on high!

Tours, Arles, and Domremy reply!
For Joan of Arc goes riding by.

The Shell

JAMES STEPHENS

And then I pressed the shell
Close to my ear
And listened well,
And straightway like a bell
Came low and clear
The slow, sad murmur of the distant seas,
Whipped by an icy breeze
Upon a shore
Wind-swept and desolate.
It was a sunless strand that never bore
The footprint of a man,
Nor felt the weight
Since time began
Of any human quality or stir
Save what the dreary winds and waves incur.
And in the hush of waters was the sound
Of pebbles rolling round,
Forever rolling with a hollow sound.
And bubbling sea-weeds as the waters go,
Swish to and fro
Their long, cold tentacles of slimy gray.
There was no day,
Nor ever came a night
Setting the stars alight
To wonder at the moon:
Was twilight only and the frightened croon,
Smitten to whimpers, of the dreary wind
And waves that journeyed blind—
And then I loosed my ear . . . O, it was sweet
To hear a cart go jolting down the street.

5

FOUR AND TWENTY BOWMEN

The Duel

EUGENE FIELD

The gingham dog and the calico cat
Side by side on the table sat;
'Twas half-past twelve, and (what do you think!)
Nor one nor t'other had slept a wink!
The old Dutch clock and the Chinese plate
Appeared to know as sure as fate
There was going to be a terrible spat.
(I wasn't there; I simply state
What was told to me by the Chinese plate!)

The gingham dog went "bow-wow-wow!"
And the calico cat replied "mee-ow!"
The air was littered, an hour or so,
With bits of gingham and calico,
While the old Dutch clock in the chimney-place
Up with its hands before its face,
For it always dreaded a family row!
(Now mind: I'm only telling you
What the old Dutch clock declares is true!)

116

The Chinese plate looked very blue.
And wailed, "Oh, dear! what shall we do!"
But the gingham dog and the calico cat
Wallowed this way and tumbled that,
Employing every tooth and claw
In the awfullest way you ever saw—
And, oh! how the gingham and calico flew!
(*Don't fancy I exaggerate!*
I got my news from the Chinese plate!)

Next morning where the two had sat
They found no trace of dog or cat;
And some folks think unto this day
That burglars stole that pair away!
But the truth about the cat and pup
Is this: They ate each other up!
Now what do you really think of that!
(*The old Dutch clock it told me so,*
And that is how I came to know.)

Soldier, Rest!

WALTER SCOTT

Soldier, rest! thy warfare o'er,
    Sleep the sleep that knows not breaking!
Dream of battled fields no more,
    Days of danger, nights of waking.
In our isle's enchanted hall,
    Hands unseen thy couch are strewing,
Fairy strains of music fall,
    Every sense in slumber dewing.
Soldier, rest! thy warfare o'er,
Dream of fighting fields no more;
Sleep the sleep that knows not breaking,
Morn of toil, nor night of waking.

No rude sound shall reach thine ear,
    Armour's clang, or war-steed champing
Trump nor pibroch summon here
    Mustering clan, or squadron tramping.
Yet the lark's shrill fife may come
    At the daybreak from the fallow,
And the bittern sound his drum,
    Booming from the sedgy shallow.
Ruder sounds shall none be near,
Guards nor warders challenge here,
Here's no war-steed's neigh and champing,
Shouting clans, or squadrons stamping.

Huntsman, rest! thy chase is done;
    While our slumbrous spells assail ye,
Dream not, with the rising sun,
    Bugles here shall sound reveillé.
Sleep! the deer is in his den;
    Sleep! thy hounds are by thee lying;
Sleep! nor dream in yonder glen,
    How thy gallant steed lay dying.
Huntsman, rest! thy chase is done,
Think not of the rising sun,
For at dawning to assail ye,
Here no bugles sound reveillé.

The Maid

THEODORE ROBERTS

Thunder of riotous hoofs over the quaking sod;
Clash of reeking squadrons, steel-capped, iron-shod;
The White Maid and the white horse, and the flapping ban-
    ner of God.

Black hearts riding for money; red hearts riding for fame;
The Maid who rides for France and the King who rides for
        shame—
Gentlemen, fools, and a saint riding in Christ's high name!

"Dust to dust!" it is written. Wind-scattered are lance and
        bow.
Dust, the Cross of Saint George; dust, the banner of snow.
The bones of the King are crumbled, and rotted the shafts of
        the foe.

Forgotten, the young knight's valour; forgotten, the captain's
        skill;
Forgotten, the fear and the hate and the mailed hands raised
        to kill;
Forgotten, the shields that clashed and the arrows that cried
        so shrill.

Like a story from some old book, that battle of long ago;
Shadows, the poor French King and the might of his English
        foe;
Shadows, the charging nobles and the archers kneeling a-row—
But a flame in my heart and my eyes, the Maid with her
        banner of snow!

A Dutch Picture

HENRY WADSWORTH LONGFELLOW

Simon Danz has come home again,
    From cruising about with his buccaneers;
He has singed the beard of the King of Spain,
And carried away the Dean of Jaen,
    And sold him in Algiers.

In his house by the Maese, with its roof of tiles,
    And weathercocks flying aloft in air,
There are silver tankards in antique styles,
Plunder of convent and castle, and piles
    Of carpets rich and rare.

In his tulip-garden there by the town,
    Overlooking the sluggish stream,
With his Moorish cap and dressing-gown,
The old sea-captain, hale and brown,
    Walks in a waking dream.

A smile in his grey mustachio lurks
    Whenever he thinks of the King of Spain,
And the listed tulips look like Turks,
And the silent gardener as he works
    Is changed to the Dean of Jaen.

The windmills on the outermost
    Verge of the landscape in the haze,
To him are towers on the Spanish coast,
With whiskered sentinels at their post,
    Though this is the river Maese.

But when the winter rains begin,
    He sits and smokes by the blazing brands,
And old seafaring men come in,
Goat-bearded, grey, and with double chin,
    And rings upon their hands.

They sit there in the shadow and shine
    Of the flickering fire of the winter night;
Figures in colour and design
Like those by Rembrandt of the Rhine,
    Half darkness and half light.

And they talk of ventures lost or won,
    And their talk is ever and ever the same,
While they drink the red wine of Tarragon,
From the cellars of some Spanish Don,
    Or convent set on flame.

Restless at times, with heavy strides
    He paces his parlour to and fro;
He is like a ship that at anchor rides,
And swings with the rising and falling tides,
    And tugs at her anchor-tow.

Voices mysteriously far and near,
    Sound of the wind and sound of the sea,
Are calling and whispering in his ear,
"Simon Danz! Why stayest thou here?
    Come forth and follow me!"

So he thinks he shall take to the sea again
    For one more cruise with his buccaneers,
To singe the beard of the King of Spain,
And capture another Dean of Jaen,
    And sell him in Algiers.

Darius Green and His Flying-Machine

JOHN TOWNSEND TROWBRIDGE

If ever there lived a Yankee lad,
Wise or otherwise, good or bad,
Who, seeing the birds fly, didn't jump
With flapping arms from stake to stump,
    Or, spreading the tail
    Of his coat for a sail,

Take a soaring leap from post to rail,
    And wonder why
    He couldn't fly,
And flap and flutter and wish and try—
    If ever you knew a country dunce
Who didn't try that as often as once,
All I can say is, that's a sign
He never would do for a hero of mine.

An aspiring genius was Darius Green:
The son of a farmer—age fourteen;
His body was long and lank and lean—
Just right for flying, as will be seen;
He had two eyes, each bright as a bean,
And a freckled nose that grew between,
A little awry—for I must mention
That he had riveted his attention
Upon his wonderful invention,
Twisting his tongue as he twisted the strings,
Working his face as he worked the wings,
And with every turn of gimlet and screw
Turning and screwing his mouth 'round, too,
    Till his nose seemed bent
    To catch the scent,
Around some corner, of new-baked pies,
And his wrinkled cheeks and his squinting eyes
Grew puckered into a queer grimace,
That made him look very droll in the face,
    And also very wise.

And wise he must have been, to do more
Than ever a genius did before,
Excepting Daedalus of yore
And his son Icarus, who wore
    Upon their backs
    Those wings of wax

He had read of in the old almanacs.
Darius was clearly of the opinion,
That the air is also man's dominion,
And that, with paddle or fin or pinion,
   We soon or late
   Should navigate
The azure as now we sail the sea.
The thing looks simple enough to me;
   And if you doubt it,
Hear how Darius reasoned about it.

      "Birds can fly,
      An' why can't I?
      Must we give in,"
      Says he with a grin,
      " 'T the bluebird an' phoebe
      Are smarter'n we be?
Jest fold our hands an' see the swaller,
An' blackbird an' catbird beat us holler?
Does the leetle, chatterin', sassy wren,
No bigger'n my thumb, know more than men?
      Jest show me that!
      Er prove't the bat
Has got more brains than's in my hat,
An' I'll back down, an' not till then!"

He argued further; "Ner I can't see
What's the use o' wings to a bumblebee,
Fer to git a livin' with, more'n to me;—
      Ain't my business
      Important's his'n is?
      That Icarus
      Was a silly cuss—
Him an' his daddy Daedalus;
They might'a' knowed wings made o' wax
Wouldn't stan' sun-heat an' hard whacks,

I'll make mine o' luther,
Er suthin' er other."

And he said to himself, as he tinkered and planned:
"But I ain't goin' to show my hand
To mummies that never can understand
The fust idee that's big an' grand.
    They'd 'a' laft an' made fun
O' Creation itself afore 't was done!"
So he kept his secret from all the rest,
Safely buttoned within his vest;
And in the loft above the shed
Himself he locked, with thimble and thread
And wax and hammer and buckles and screws,
All such things as geniuses use;—
Two bats for patterns, curious fellows!
A charcoal-pot and a pair of bellows;
An old hoop-skirt or two, as well as
Some wire and several old umbrellas;
A carriage-cover, for tail and wings;
A piece of harness; and straps and strings;
    And a big strong box,
    In which he locks
These and a hundred other things.

His grinning brothers, Reuben and Burke
And Nathan and Jotham and Solomon, lurk
Around the corner to see him work—
Sitting cross-legged, like a Turk,
Drawing the waxed-end through with a jerk,
And boring the holes with a comical quirk
Of his wise old head, and a knowing smirk.
But vainly they mounted each other's backs,
And poked through knot-holes and pried through cracks;
With wood from the pile and straw from the stacks
He plugged the knot-holes and calked the cracks;

124

And a bucket of water, which one would think
He had brought up into the loft to drink
    When he chanced to be dry,
    Stood always nigh,
    For Darius was sly;
And whenever at work he happened to spy
At chink or crevice a blinking eye,
He let a dipper of water fly.
"Take that! an' ef ever ye get a peep,
Guess ye'll ketch a weasel asleep!"
    And he sings as he locks
    His big strong box:

"The weasel's head is small an' trim
An' he is leetle an' long an' slim,
An' quick of motion an' nimble of limb,
    An' ef yeou'll be
    Advised by me,
Keep wide awake when ye're ketchin' him!"

    So day after day
He stitched and tinkered and hammered away,
    Till at last 'twas done—
The greatest invention under the sun!
"An' now," says Darius, "hooray fer some fun!"

    'Twas the Fourth of July,
    And the weather was dry,
And not a cloud was on all the sky,
Save a few light fleeces, which here and there,
    Half mist, half air,
Like foam on the ocean went floating by:
Just as lovely a morning as ever was seen
For a nice little trip in a flying-machine.
Thought cunning Darius: "Now I shan't go
Along 'ith the fellers to see the show.

I'll say I've got sich a terrible cough!
An' then, when the folks 'ave all gone off,
    I'll hev full swing
    For to try the thing,
An' practyse a leetle on the wing."

"Ain't goin' to see the celebration?"
Says Brother Nate. "No; botheration!
I've got sich a cold—a toothache—I—
My gracious!—feel's though I should fly!"
    Said Jotham, "Sho!
    Guess ye better go."
    But Darius said, "No!
Shouldn't wonder 'f yeou might see me, though,
'Long 'bout noon, ef I git red
O' this jumpin', thumpin' pain 'n my head."
For all the while to himself he said:

    "I'll tell ye what!
I'll fly a few times around the lot,
To see how 't seems, then soon's I've got
The hang o' the thing, ez likely's not,
    I'll astonish the nation,
    And all creation,
By flying over the celebration!
Over their heads I'll sail like an eagle;
I'll balance myself on my wings like a sea-gull;
I'll dance on the chimbleys; I'll stan' on the steeple;
I'll flop up to the winders an' scare the people!
I'll light on the libbe'ty-pole, an' crow;
An' I'll say to the gawpin' fools below,
    'What world's this 'ere
    That I've come near?'
For I'll make 'em believe I'm a chap f'm the moon!
An' I'll try a race 'ith their ol' balloon."
    He crept from his bed;

And, seeing the others were gone, he said,
"I'm a gittin' over the cold 'n my head."
　　And away he sped,
To open the wonderful box in the shed.

His brothers had walked but a little way
When Jotham to Nathan chanced to say,
"What on airth is he up to, hey?"
"Don'o'—the' 's suthin' er other to pay,
Er he wouldn't 'a' stayed to hum today."
Says Burke, "His toothache's all 'n his eye!
He never'd miss a Fo'th-'o-July,
Ef he hadn't got some machine to try.
Le's hurry back an' hide in the barn,
An' pay him fer tellin' us that yarn!"
"Agreed!" Through the orchard they creep back,
Along by the fences, behind the stack,
And one by one, through a hole in the wall,
In under the dusty barn they crawl,
Dressed in their Sunday garments all;
And a very astonishing sight was that,
When each in his cobwebbed coat and hat
Came up through the floor like an ancient rat.
　　And there they hid;
　　And Reuben slid
The fastenings back, and the door undid.
　　"Keep dark!" said he,
"While I squint an' see what the' is to see."

As knights of old put on their mail—
　　From head to foot
　　An iron suit,
Iron jacket and iron boot,
Iron breeches, and on the head
No hat, but an iron pot instead,
　　And under the chin the bail—

(I believe they call thc thing a helm;)
And the lid they carried they called a shield;
And, thus accoutred, they took the field,
Sallying forth to overwhelm
The dragons and pagans that plagued the realm;
     So this modern knight
     Prepared for flight,
Put on his wings and strapped them tight;
Jointed and jaunty, strong and light;
Buckled them fast to shoulder and hip—
Ten feet they measured from tip to tip!
And a helm had he, but that he wore,
Not on his head like those of yore,
     But more like the helm of a ship.

     "Hush!" Reuben said,
     "He's up in the shed!
He's opened the winder—I see his head!
     He stretches it out,
     An' pokes it about,
Lookin' to see 'f the coast is clear,
     An' nobody near;—
Guess he don'o' who's hid in here!
He's riggin' a spring-board over the sill!
Stop laffin', Solomon! Burke, keep still!
He's a-climbin' out now—of all the things!
What's he got on? I vum, it's wings!
An' that 'tother thing? I vum it's a tail!
An' there he sets like a hawk on a rail!
Steppin' careful, he travels the length
Of his spring-board, and teeters to try its strength.
Now he stretches his wings, like a monstrous bat;
Peeks over his shoulder, this way an' that,
Fer to see 'f the' 's anyone passin' by;
But the' 's on'y a ca'f an' a goslin' nigh.
They turn up at him a wonderin' eye,
128

To see—The dragon! he's goin' to fly!
Away he goes! Jimminy! what a jump!
    Flop flop an' plump
    To the ground with a thump!
Flutt'rin' an' flound'rin', all in a lump!"

As a demon is hurled by an angel's spear,
Heels over head, to his proper sphere—
Heels over head, and head over heels,
Dizzily down the abyss he wheels—
So fell Darius. Upon his crown,
In the midst of the barnyard, he came down,
In a wonderful whirl of tangled strings,
Broken braces and broken springs,
Broken tail and broken wings,
Shooting-stars, and various things!
Away with a bellow fled the calf,
And what was that? Did the gosling laugh?
    'Tis a merry roar
    From the old barn-door,
And he hears the voice of Jotham crying,
"Say, D'rius! how de yeou like flyin'?"
Slowly, ruefully, where he lay,
Darius just turned and looked that way,
As he stanched his sorrowful nose with his cuff.
"Wall, I like flyin' well enough,"
He said; "but the' ain't sich a thunderin' sight
O' fun in 't when ye come to light."

I just have room for the moral here;
And this is the moral—Stick to your sphere.
Or if you insist, as you have the right,
On spreading your wings for a loftier flight,
The moral is—Take care how you light.

The Ballad of the Oysterman

OLIVER WENDELL HOLMES

It was a tall young oysterman lived by the river-side,
His shop was just upon the bank, his boat was on the tide;
The daughter of a fisherman, that was so straight and slim,
Lived over on the other bank, right opposite to him.

It was the pensive oysterman that saw a lovely maid,
Upon a moonlit evening, a-sitting in the shade;
He saw her wave her handkerchief, as much as if to say,
"I'm wide awake, young oysterman, and all the folks away."

Then up arose the oysterman, and to himself said he,
"I guess I'll leave the skiff at home, for fear that folks should
    see;
I read it in the story-book, that, for to kiss his dear,
Leander swam the Hellespont,—and I will swim this here."

And he has leaped into the waves, and crossed the shining
    stream,
And he has clambered up the bank, all in the moonlight
    gleam;
Oh, there were kisses sweet as dew, and words as soft as
    rain,—
But they have heard her father's step, and in he leaps again!

Out spoke the ancient fisherman: "Oh, what was that, my
    daughter?"
" 'Twas nothing but a pebble, sir, I threw into the water."
"And what is that, pray tell me, love, that paddles off so
    fast?"
"It's nothing but a porpoise, sir, that's been a-swimming
    past."

Out spoke the ancient fisherman: "Now bring me my
    harpoon!
I'll get into my fishing boat, and fix the fellow soon."
Down fell the pretty innocent, as falls a snow-white lamb;
Her hair drooped round her pallid cheeks, like seaweed on
    a clam.

Alas for those two loving ones! She waked not from her
    swound,
And he was taken with a cramp, and in the waves was
    drowned;
But fate has metamorphosed them, in pity of their woe,
And now they keep an oyster-shop for mermaids down below.

The Deacon's Masterpiece

OLIVER WENDELL HOLMES

Have you heard of the wonderful one-hoss shay,
That was built in such a logical way
It ran a hundred years to a day,
And then, of a sudden, it—ah, but stay,
I'll tell you what happened without delay:
Scaring the parson into fits,
Frightening people out of their wits—
Have you ever heard of that, I say?

Seventeen hundred and fifty-five;
Georgius Secundus was then alive,—
Snuffy old drone from the German hive.
That was the year when Lisbon-town
Saw the earth open and gulp her down,
And Braddock's army was done so brown,
Left without a scalp to its crown.
It was the terrible Earthquake day
That the Deacon finished the one-hoss shay.

Now in building chaises, I tell you what,
There is always *somewhere* a weakest spot,—
In hub, tire, felloe, in spring or thill,
In panel, or cross-bar, or floor, or sill,
In screw, bolt, thoroughbrace,—lurking still,
Find it somewhere you must and will,—
Above or below, or within or without,—
And that's the reason, beyond a doubt,
That a chaise *breaks down*, but doesn't *wear out.*

But the Deacon swore (as Deacons do,
With an "I dew vum," or an "I tell *yeou*")
He would build one shay to beat the taown
'N' the keounty 'n' all the kentry raoun';
It should be so built that it couldn't break daown:
"Fur," said the Deacon, " 't's mighty plain
Thut the weakes' place mus' stan' the strain;
'N' the way t' fix it, uz I maintain,
            Is only jest
T' make that place uz strong uz the rest."

So the Deacon inquired of the village folk
Where he could find the strongest oak,
That couldn't be split nor bent nor broke,—
That was for spokes and floor and sills;
He sent for lancewood to make the thills;
The crossbars were ash, from the straightest trees;
The panels of white-wood, that cuts like cheese,
But lasts like iron for things like these;

The hubs of logs from the "Settler's ellum,"
Last of its timber,—they couldn't sell 'em,—
Never an axe had seen their chips,
And the wedges flew from between their lips,
Their blunt ends frizzled like celery-tips;
Step and prop-iron, bolt and screw,

132

Spring, tire, axle, and linch-pin too,
Steel of the finest, bright and blue;
Thoroughbrace bison-skin, thick and wide;
Boot, top, dasher, from tough old hide
Found in the pit when the tanner died.
That was the way he "put her through."
"There!" said the Deacon, "Noaw she'll dew!"

Do! I tell you, I rather guess
She was a wonder, and nothing less!
Colts grew horses, beards turned gray,
Deacon and deaconess dropped away,
Children and grandchildren—where were they?
But there stood the stout old one-hoss shay
As fresh as on Lisbon-earthquake day!

Eighteen hundred;—it came and found
The Deacon's masterpiece strong and sound.
Eighteen hundred increased by ten;—
"Hahnsum kerridge" they called it then.
Eighteen hundred and twenty came;—
Running as usual; much the same.
Thirty and forty at last arrive,
And then come fifty, and *fifty-five*.

Little of all we value here
Wakes on the morn of its hundredth year
Without both feeling and looking queer.
In fact, there's nothing that keeps its youth,
So far as I know, but a tree and truth.
(This is a moral that runs at large;
Take it.—You're welcome.—No extra charge.)

First of November,—the Earthquake day,—

There are traces of age in the one-hoss shay,
A general flavour of mild decay,
But nothing local, as one may say.
There couldn't be,—for the Deacon's art
Had made it so like in every part
That there wasn't a chance for one to start.
For the wheels were just as strong as the thills,
And the floor was just as strong as the sills,
And the panels just as strong as the floor,
And the whipple-tree neither less nor more,
And the back cross-bar as strong as the fore,
And spring and axle and hub *encore*.
And yet, as a *whole*, it is past a doubt
In another hour it will be *worn out!*

First of November, 'Fifty-five!
This morning the parson takes a drive.
Now, small boys, gct out of the way!
Here comes the wonderful one-hoss shay,
Drawn by a rat-tailed, ewe-necked bay.
"Huddup!" said the parson.—Off went they.

The parson was working his Sunday text,—
Had got to *fifthly*, and stopped perplexed
At what the—Moses—was coming next.
All at once the horse stood still,
Close by the meet'n'-house on the hill.
First a shiver, and then a thrill,
Then something decidedly like a spill,
And the parson was sitting upon a rock,
At half-past nine by the meet'n'-house clock,—
Just the hour of the Earthquake shock!
What do you think the parson found,
When he got up and stared around?
The poor old chaise in a heap or mound,
As if it had been to the mill and ground!

You see, of course, if you're not a dunce,
How it went to pieces all at once,—
All at once, and nothing first,
Just as bubbles do when they burst.

End of the wonderful one-hoss shay.
Logic is logic. That's all I say.

The Old Buccaneer

CHARLES KINGSLEY

Oh England is a pleasant place for them that's rich and high,
But England is a cruel place for such poor folks as I;
And such a port for mariners I ne'er shall see again
As the pleasant Isle of Avès, beside the Spanish main.

There were forty craft in Avès that were both swift and stout,
All furnished well with small arms and cannons round about;
And a thousand men in Avès made laws so fair and free
To choose their valiant captains and obey them loyally.

Thence we sailed against the Spaniard with his hoards of
        plate and gold,
Which he wrung with cruel tortures from Indian folk of old;
Likewise the merchant captains, with hearts as hard as stone,
Who flog men, and keel-haul them, and starve them to the
        bone.

O the palms grew high in Avès, and fruits that shone like
        gold,
And the colibris and parrots they were gorgeous to behold;
And the negro maids to Avès from bondage fast did flee,
To welcome gallant sailors, a-sweeping in from sea.

135

O sweet it was in Avès to hear the landward breeze,
A-swing with good tobacco in a net between the trees,
With a negro lass to fan you, while you listened to the roar
Of the breakers on the reef outside, that never touched the
    shore.

But Scripture saith, an ending to all fine things must be;
So the King's ships sailed on Avès, and quite put down were
    we.
All day we fought like bulldogs, but they burst the booms at
    night;
And I fled in a piragua, sore wounded, from the fight.

Nine days I floated starving, and a negro lass beside,
Till, for all I tried to cheer her, the poor young thing she
    died;
But as I lay a-gasping, a Bristol sail came by,
And brought me home to England here, to beg until I die.

And now I'm old and going—I'm sure I can't tell where;
One comfort is, this world's so hard, I can't be worse off
    there:
If I might but be a sea-dove, I'd fly across the main,
To the pleasant Isle of Avès, to look at it once again.

The Yarn of the Nancy Bell

WILLIAM S. GILBERT

'Twas on the shores that round our coast
From Deal to Ramsgate span,
That I found alone on a piece of stone
An elderly naval man.

His hair was weedy, his beard was long,
And weedy and long was he,
And I heard this wight on the shore recite,
In a singular minor key;

"Oh, I am a cook, and the captain bold,
And the mate of the *Nancy* brig
And a bo'sun tight, and a midshipmite,
And the crew of the captain's gig!"

And he shook his fists and he tore his hair,
Till I really felt afraid,
For I couldn't help thinking the man had been drinking,
And so I simply said;

"Oh elderly man, it's little I know
Of the duties of men of the sea,
But I'll eat my hand if I understand
How you can possibly be

"At once a cook, and a captain bold,
And the mate of the *Nancy* brig,
And a bo'sun tight, and a midshipmite,
And the crew of the captain's gig."

Then he gave a hitch to his trousers, which
Is a trick all seamen larn,
And having got rid of a thumping quid,
He spun this painful yarn;

" 'Twas in the good ship *Nancy Bell*
That we sailed to the Indian sea,
And there on a reef we came to grief,
Which has often occurred to me.

"And pretty nigh all o' the crew was drowned
(There was seventy-seven o' soul),
And only ten of the *Nancy's* men
Said 'Here' to the muster roll.

"There was me and the cook and the captain bold
And the mate of the *Nancy* brig,
And the bo'sun tight, and a midshipmite,
And the crew of the captain's gig.

"For a month we'd neither wittles nor drink,
Till a-hungary we did feel,
So we drawed a lot, and accordin' shot
The captain for our meal.

"The next lot fell to the *Nancy's* mate,
And a delicate dish he made;
Then our appetite with the midshipmite
We seven survivors stayed.

"And then we murdered the bo'sun tight,
And he much resembled pig;
Then we wittled free, did the cook and me,
On the crew of the captain's gig.

"Then only the cook and me was left,
And the delicate question 'which
Of us two goes to the kettle?' arose
And we argued it out as sich.

"For I loved that cook as a brother, I did,
And the cook he worshipped me;
But we'd both be blowed if we'd either be stowed
In the other chap's hold, you see.

138

'I'll be eat if you dines off me,' says Tom,
'Yes, that,' says I, 'you'll be!'
'I'm boiled if I die, my friend,' quoth I,
And 'Exactly so!' quoth he.

"Says he, 'Dear James, to murder me
Were a foolish thing to do,
For don't you see that you can't cook me,
While I can—and will—cook you?'

"So he boils the water and takes the salt
And the pepper in portions true
(Which he never forgot), and some chopped shalot,
And some sage and parsley, too.

" 'Come here,' says he, with proper pride,
Which his smiling features tell,
' 'Twill soothing be if I let you see,
How extremely nice you'll smell.'

"And he stirred it round and round and round
And he sniffed at the foaming froth;
When I ups with his heels, and smothers his squeals
In the scum of the boiling broth.

"And I eat that cook in a week or less,
And—as I eating be
The last of his chops, why, I almost drops,
For a vessel in sight I see.

"And I never grieve, and I never smile,
And I never larf nor play
But I sit and croak, and a single joke
I have—which is to say;

"Oh, I am a cook, and a captain bold,
And the mate of the *Nancy* brig,
And a bos'un tight, and a midshipmite,
And the crew of the captain's gig!"

The Legends of Evil

RUDYARD KIPLING

I

This is the sorrowful story
　　Told as the twilight fails
And the monkeys walk together
　　Holding their neighbor's tails:—

"Our fathers lived in the forest,
　　Foolish people were they,
They went down to the cornland
　　To teach the farmers to play.

"Our fathers frisked in the millet,
　　Our fathers skipped in the wheat,
Our fathers hung from the branches
　　Our fathers danced in the street.

"Then came the terrible farmers,
　　Nothing of play they knew,
Only . . . they caught our fathers
　　And set them to labor too!

"Set them to work in the cornland
　　With ploughs and sickles and flails,
Put them in mud-walled prisons
　　And—cut off their beautiful tails!

"Now we can watch our fathers,
  Sullen and bowed and old,
Stooping over the millet,
  Sharing the silly mould,

"Driving a foolish furrow,
  Mending a muddy yoke,
Sleeping in mud-walled prisons,
  Steeping their food in smoke.

"We may not speak with our fathers,
  For if the farmers knew
They would come up to the forest
  And set us to labor too."

This is the horrible story
  Told as the twilight fails
And the monkeys walk together
  Holding their neighbor's tails.

II

'Twas when the rain fell steady an' the Ark was pitched an'
    ready,
  That Noah got his orders for to take the bastes below;
He dragged them all together by the horn an' hide an' feather,
  An' all excipt the Donkey was agreeable to go.

Thin Noah spoke him fairly, thin talked to him sevarely,
  An' thin he cursed him squarely to the glory av the
    Lord:—
"Divil take the ass that bred you, and the greater ass that fed
    you—
  "Divil go wid you, ye spalpeen!" an' the Donkey wint
    aboard.

But the wind was always failin', an' 'twas most onaisy sailin',
   An' the ladies in the cabin couldn't stand the stable air;
An' the bastes betwuxt the hatches, they tuk an' died in
      batches,
      Till Noah said:—"There's wan av us that hasn't paid his
      fare!"

For he heard a flusteration 'mid the bastes av all creation—
   The trumpetin' av elephants an' bellowing av whales;
An' he saw forninst the windy when he wint to stop the
      shindy
      The Divil wid a stable-fork bedivillin' their tails.

The Divil cursed outrageous, but Noah said umbrageous:—
   "To what am I indebted for this tenant-right invasion?"
An' the Divil gave for answer:—"Evict me if you can, sir,
   "For I came in wid the Donkey—on Your Honour's invi-
      tation."

Bugs

WILL STOKES

Oh, the gen'ral raised the devil with the kernel, so 'tis said,
About a little hitch in the formation at parade,
An' the kernel told the major that his handlin' the battalion
Resimbled a soci'ty-man a-leadin' a cotillion,
An' the major hauled the cap'en up about some oversight
Manooverin' the company while breakin' from the right,
An' the cap'en gravely caushun'd the lootenant b'ar in mind
To keep the rear rank well closed up an' properly ali'ned.

         Oh, them big bugs have bigger bugs
            That jump on 'em an' bite 'em,
         An' the bigger bugs have other bugs
            An' so—ad infinitum.

The sergeant made a break an' the lootenant collared him,
Politely intimatin' that he didn't know a dem,
An' the sergeant soon an error in preservin' distance spied
An' took a shot at Darringer, the cop'ril, who was guide,
But Darringer said nuthin'—he just waited for his chance
An' promptly gave some scorchin' views on tactics to the
    lance,
Who opened fire on private Dean for spilin' all the wheels
An' Dean cussed Smith, his rear rank man, for steppin' on
    his heels.

        Oh, them big bugs have bigger bugs
           That jump on 'em an' bite 'em,
      An' the bigger bugs have other bugs
           An' so—*ad infinitum.*

'Twas all wound up in barracks when the reg'ment was dis-
    missed,
An' Dean's eye accidentally ran foul o' Smithy's fist,
An' we stood on chairs an' tables, an' we backed 'em for the
    beer,
While the clamor o' the battle woke the echoes far an' near.
It was jest a rough-an'-tumble but a most instructiv' fight,
Till the sergeant an' a detail o' the guard marched into sight,
An' they tuk 'em blown an' bloody, an' they locked 'em in
    the mill,
An'—that's all I remember o' the Big Review an' Drill.

        'Cept that big bugs have bigger bugs
           That jump on 'em and bite 'em,
      An' the bigger bugs have other bugs
           An' so—*ad infinitum.*

Robin Hood and Allin a Dale

OLD BALLAD

Come listen to me, you gallants so free,
    All you that love mirth for to hear,
And I will tell you of a bold outlaw
    That lived in Nottinghamshire.

As Robin Hood in the forest stood,
    All under the greenwood tree,
There he was aware of a brave young man
    As fine as fine might be.

The youngster was cloth'd in scarlet red,
    In scarlet fine and gay;
And he did frisk it over the plain,
    And chanted a roundelay.

As Robin Hood next morning stood
    Amongst the leaves so gay,
There did he espy the same young man,
    Come drooping along the way.

The scarlet he wore the day before
    It was clean cast away;
And at every step he fetch'd a sigh,
    'Alack and a well-a-day!'

Then stepp'd forth brave Little John,
    And Midge, the miller's son,
Which made the young man bend his bow,
    When as he saw them come.

'Stand off, stand off!' the young man said,
    'What is your will with me?'

'You must come before our master straight,
	Under yon greenwood tree.'

And when he came bold Robin before,
	Robin asked him courteously,
'O, hast thou any money to spare
	For my merry men and me?'

'I have no money,' the young man said,
	'But five shillings and a ring;
And that I have kept this seven long years,
	To have it at my wedding.

'Yesterday I should have married a maid,
	But she soon from me was tane,
And chosen to be an old knight's delight,
	Whereby my poor heart is slain.'

'What is thy name?' then said Robin Hood,
	'Come tell me without any fail:'
'By the faith of my body,' then said the young man
'My name it is Allin a Dale.'

'What wilt thou give me?' said Robin Hood,
	'In ready gold or fee,
To help thee to thy true love again,
	And deliver her unto thee?'

'I have no money,' then quoth the young man,
	'No ready gold nor fee,
But I will swear upon a book
	Thy true servant for to be!'

'How many miles is it to thy true love?
	Come tell me without guile:'
'By the faith of my body,' then said the young man,
	'It is but a little mile.'

Then Robin he hasted over the plain,
    He did neither stint nor lin,
Until he came unto the church,
    Where Allin should keep his wedding.

'What hast thou here?' the bishop then said,
    'I prithee now tell unto me:'
'I am a bold harper,' quoth Robin Hood,
    'And the best in the north country.'

'O welcome, O welcome,' the bishop he said.
    'That music best pleaseth me;'
'You shall have no music,' quoth Robin Hood,
    'Till the bride and the bridegroom I see.'

With that came in a wealthy knight,
    Which was both grave and old,
And after him a finikin lass,
    Did shine like the glistering gold.

'This is not a fit match,' quoth bold Robin Hood,
    'That you do seem to make here,
For since we are come into the church
    The bride shall choose her own dear.'

Then Robin Hood put his horn to his mouth,
    And blew blasts two or three;
When four-and-twenty bowmen bold
    Came leaping over the lea.

And when they came into the churchyard,
    Marching all on a row,
The very first man was Allin a Dale,
    To give bold Robin his bow,

'This is thy true love,' Robin he said,
    'Young Allin as I hear say;
And you shall be married at this same time,
    Before we depart away.'

'That shall not be,' the bishop he said,
    'For thy word shall not stand;
They shall be three times asked in the church,
    As the law is of our land.'

Robin Hood pulled off the bishop's coat,
    And put it upon Little John;
'By the faith of my body,' then Robin said,
    'This cloth doth make thee a man.'

When Little John went into the quire,
    The people began to laugh;
He asked them seven times in the church,
    Lest three times should not be enough.

'Who gives me this maid?' said Little John:
    Quoth Robin Hood, 'That do I,
And he that takes her from Allin a Dale,
    Full dearly he shall her buy.'

And thus having end of this merry wedding,
    The bride looked like a queen;
And so they returned to the merry greenwood,
    Amongst the leaves so green.

Daniel Boone

ARTHUR GUITERMAN

Daniel Boone at twenty-one
Came with his tomahawk, knife, and gun
Home from the French and Indian War
To North Carolina and the Yadkin shore.
He married his maid with a golden band,
Builded his house and cleared his land;
But the deep woods claimed their son again
And he turned his face from the homes of men.
Over the Blue Ridge, dark and lone,
The Mountains of Iron, the Hills of Stone,
Braving the Shawnee's jealous wrath,
He made his way on the Warrior's Path.
Alone he trod the shadowed trails;
But he was lord of a thousand vales
As he roved Kentucky, far and near,
Hunting the buffalo, elk and deer.
What joy to see, what joy to win
So fair a land for his kith and kin,
Of streams unstained and woods unhewn!
"Elbow room!" laughed Daniel Boone.

On the Wilderness Road that his axmen made
The settlers flocked to the first stockade;
The deerskin shirts and the coonskin caps
Filed through the glens and the mountain gaps;
And hearts were high in the fateful spring
When the land said "Nay!" to the stubborn king.
While the men of the East of farm and town
Strove with the troops of the British Crown,
Daniel Boone from a surge of hate
Guarded a nation's westward gate.
Down in the fort in a wave of flame

The Shawnee horde and the Mingo came,
And the stout logs shook in a storm of lead;
But Boone stood firm and the savage fled.
Peace! And the settlers flocked anew,
The farm lands spread, and the town lands grew;
But Daniel Boone was ill at ease
When he saw the smoke in his forest trees.
"There'll be no game in the country soon.
Elbow room!" cried Daniel Boone.

Straight as a pine at sixty-five—
Time enough for a man to thrive—
He launched his bateau on Ohio's breast
And his heart was glad as he oared it west;
There was kindly folk and his own true blood
Where the great Missouri rolls his flood;
New woods, new streams, and room to spare,
And Daniel Boone found comfort there.
Yet far he ranged toward the sunset still,
Where the Kansas runs and the Smoky Hill,
And the prairies toss, by the south wind blown;
And he killed his bear on the Yellowstone.
But ever he dreamed of new domains
With vaster woods and wider plains;
Ever he dreamed of a world-to-be
Where there are no bounds and the soul is free.
At fourscore-five, still stout and hale,
He heard a call to a farther trail;
So he turned his face where the stars are strewn;
"Elbow room!" sighed Daniel Boone.

Down the Milky Way in its banks of blue
Far he has paddled his white canoe
To the splendid quest of the tameless soul—
He has reached the goal where there is no goal.
Now he rides and rides an endless trail

On the hippogriff of the flaming tail
Or the horse of the stars with the golden mane,
As he rode the first of the blue-grass strain.
The joy that lies in the search he seeks
On breathless hills with crystal peaks;
He makes his camp on heights untrod,
The steps of the shrine, alone with God.
Through the woods of the vast, on the plains of space
He hunts the pride of the mammoth race
And the dinosaur of the triple horn,
The manticore and the unicorn,
As once by the broad Missouri's flow
He followed the elk and the buffalo.
East of the sun and west of the moon,
"Elbow room!" laughs Daniel Boone.

6

YONDER SEE THE MORNING BLINK

Yonder See the Morning Blink

A. E. HOUSMAN

Yonder see the morning blink:
    The sun is up, and up must I,
To wash and dress and eat and drink
And look at things and talk and think
    And work, and God knows why.

Oh often have I washed and dressed
    And what's to show for all my pain?
Let me lie abed and rest:
Ten thousand times I've done my best
    And all's to do again.

Keeping On

A. H. CLOUGH

Say not the struggle nought availeth,
  The labour and the wounds are vain,
The enemy faints not, nor faileth,
  And as things have been they remain.

If hopes were dupes, fears may be liars;
  It may be, in yon smoke concealed,
Your comrades chase e'en now the fliers,
  And, but for you, possess the field.

For while the tired waves, vainly breaking,
  Seem here no painful inch to gain,
Far back, through creeks and inlets making,
  Comes silent, flooding in, the main.

And not by eastern windows only,
  When daylight comes, comes in the light;
In front the sun climbs slow, how slowly!
  But westward, look, the land is bright!

The Panther

OGDEN NASH

The panther is like a leopard,
Except it hasn't been peppered,
Should you behold a panther crouch,
Prepare to say Ouch.
Better yet, if called by a panther,
Don't anther.

Fish to Man

LEIGH HUNT

Amazing monster! that, for aught I know,
With the first sight of thee didst make our race
For ever stare! O flat and shocking face,
Grimly divided from the breast below!
Thou that on dry land horribly dost go
With a split body and most ridiculous pace,
Prong after prong, disgracer of all grace,
Long useless-finned, haired, upright, unwet, slow!

O breather of unbreathable, sword-sharp air,
How canst exist? How bear thyself, thou dry
And dreary sloth! What particle canst share
Of the only blessed life, the watery?
I sometimes see of ye an actual *pair*
Go by! linked fin by fin! most odiously.

Luck

WILFRED GIBSON

What brings you, sailor, home from the sea—
Coffers of gold and of ivory?

When first I went to sea as a lad
A new jack-knife was all I had;

And I've sailed for fifty years and three
To the coasts of gold and of ivory;

And now at the end of a lucky life,
Well, still I've got my old jack-knife.

154

There Was a Naughty Boy

JOHN KEATS

There was a naughty boy
And a naughty boy was he.
He ran away to Scotland,
The people for to see.
    But he found
    That the ground
    Was as hard,
    That a yard
    Was as long,
    That a song
    Was as merry,
    That a cherry
    Was as red,
    That lead
    Was as weighty,
    That four-score
    Was still eighty,
    And a door was as wooden as in England.
So he stood in his shoes and he wondered,
He wondered, he wondered,
So he stood in his shoes and he wondered.

An Epitaph

AUTHOR UNKNOWN

Under this sod and beneath these trees
Lies all that's left of Samuel Pease.
Pease ain't here,
It's just his pod;
He shelled out his soul
Which flew to God.

Time, You Old Gypsy Man

RALPH HODGSON

Time, you old gypsy man,
Will you not stay,
Put up your caravan
Just for one day?

All things I'll give you
Will you be my guest,
Bells for your jennet
Of silver the best,
Goldsmiths shall beat you
A great golden ring,
Peacocks shall bow to you,
Little boys sing,
Oh, and sweet girls will
Festoon you with may.
Time, you old gypsy,
Why hasten away?

Last week in Babylon,
Last night in Rome,
Morning, and in the crush
Under Paul's dome;
Under Paul's dial
You tighten your rein—
Only a moment,
And off once again;
Off to some city
Now blind in the womb,
Off to another
Ere that's in the tomb.

Time, you old gypsy man,
Will you not stay,
Put up your caravan
Just for one day?

At a Country Fair

JOHN HOLMES

Wrinkling with laughter that made no sound
    In the high brass blare,
An old man rode on the merry-go-round
    At a country fair.

Duty all past, and past all hurt
    Of his years four-score,
He rowelled the painted horse to spurt
    One lap, and one more.

So round to the music, all wonder and wild,
    Rode the piebald pair,
Overtaking and passing a country child
    Who stood to stare.

Time and its angels could be outdone,
    And tomorrow's wind,
With the right man mounted and good for the run;
    And the old man grinned.

Let the night come on, and the world go wide.
    Let the burying-ground
Be dug and be damned. He'd ride
    On the merry-go-round,
    On the merry-go-round.

The Zoo

HUMBERT WOLFE

I scarcely think
    I like the Zoo
as much as other
    people do.

First when I see
    the elephants,
they seem in trouble
    with their pants,

and then the hippo-
    potamus
says "Who in blazes
    made me thus?"

And I observe the
    chimpanzee
thanking his God
    he's not like me.

While all varieties
    of cat,
make me feel dumpy,
    coarse and fat.

And that's not all!
    The eagles make
me stare as though
    my heart would break

at the great spaces
    of the air.

And why, it isn't
    my affair

if hippo is a
    sort of evil
joke perpetrated
    by the devil,

and of all broken-
    hearted things
the brokenest are
    captive wings!

And yet I can-
    not like the Zoo
as much as other
    people do.

Prelude

T. S. ELIOT

The winter evening settles down
With smells of steaks in passageways.
Six o'clock.
The burnt-out end of smoky days.
And now a gusty shower wraps
The grimy scraps
Of withered leaves about your feet
And newspapers from vacant lots;
The showers beat
On broken blinds and chimney-pots,
And at the corner of the street
A lonely cab-horse steams and stamps.
And then the lighting of the lamps.

The Mouse

ELIZABETH COATSWORTH

I heard a mouse
Bitterly complaining
In a crack of moonlight
Aslant on the floor—

"Little I ask,
And that little is not granted;
There are few crumbs
In this world any more.

"The bread box is tin
And I cannot get in.

"The jam's in a jar
My teeth cannot mar.

"The cheese sits by itself
On the ice-box shelf.

"All night I run
Searching and seeking;
All night I run
About on the floor.

"Moonlight is there
And a bare place for dancing,
But no little feast
Is spread any more."

Widdicombe Fair

OLD BALLAD

"Tom Pearse, Tom Pearse, lend me your gray mare,
  All along, down along, out along, lee.
For I want to go to Widdicombe Fair,
    Wi' Bill Brewer, Jan Stewer, Peter Gurney, Peter Davy,
    Dan'l Whiddon, Harry Hawk,
Old Uncle Tom Cobleigh and all,
    Old Uncle Tom Cobleigh and all."

"And when shall I see again my gray mare?"
  All along, down along, out along, lee.
"By Friday soon, or Saturday noon,
    Wi' Bill Brewer, Jan Stewer, Peter Gurney, Peter Davy,
    Dan'l Whiddon, Harry Hawk,
Old Uncle Tom Cobleigh and all.
    Old Uncle Tom Cobleigh and all."

Then Friday came and Saturday noon,
  All along, down along, out along, lee.
But Tom Pearse's old mare hath not trotted home,
    Wi' Bill Brewer, Jan Stewer, Peter Gurney, Peter Davy,
    Dan'l Whiddon, Harry Hawk,
Old Uncle Tom Cobleigh and all.
    Old Uncle Tom Cobleigh and all.

So Tom Pearse he got up to the top o' the hill,
  All along, down along, out along, lee.
And he sees his old mare down a-making her will,
    Wi' Bill Brewer, Jan Stewer, Peter Gurney, Peter Davy,
    Dan'l Whiddon, Harry Hawk,
Old Uncle Tom Cobleigh and all!
    Old Uncle Cobleigh and all.

So Tom Pearse's old mare her took sick and her died,
    All along, down along, out along, lee.
And Tom he sat down on a stone, and he cried
      Wi' Bill Brewer, Jan Stewer, Peter Gurney, Peter Davy,
      Dan'l Whiddon, Harry Hawk,
Old Uncle Tom Cobleigh and all.
    Old Uncle Cobleigh and all.

But this isn't the end o' this shocking affair,
    All along, down along, out along, lee.
Nor, though they be dead, of the horrid career
      Of Bill Brewer, Jan Stewer, Peter Gurney, Peter Davy,
      Dan'l Whiddon, Harry Hawk,
Old Uncle Tom Cobleigh and all.
    Old Uncle Cobleigh and all.

When the wind whistles cold on the moor of a night,
    All along, down along, out along, lee.
Tom Pearse's old mare doth appear, ghastly white,
      Wi' Bill Brewer, Jan Stewer, Peter Gurney, Peter Davy,
      Dan'l Whiddon, Harry Hawk,
Old Uncle Tom Cobleigh and all.
    Old Uncle Cobleigh and all.

And all the long night he heard skirling and groans,
    All along, down along, out along, lee.
From Tom Pearse's old mare in her rattling bones,
      And from Bill Brewer, Jan Stewer, Peter Gurney, Peter
        Davy,
      Dan'l Whiddon, Harry Hawk,
Old Uncle Tom Cobleigh and all.
    OLD UNCLE TOM COBLEIGH AND ALL.

The Purist

OGDEN NASH

I give you now Professor Twist,
A conscientious scientist.
Trustees exclaimed, "He never bungles!"
And sent him off to distant jungles.
Camped on a tropic riverside,
One day he missed his loving bride.
She had, the guide informed him later,
Been eaten by an alligator.
Professor Twist could not but smile.
"You mean," he said, "a crocodile."

Hope Is the Thing With Feathers

EMILY DICKINSON

Hope is the thing with feathers
That perches in the soul,
And sings the tune without the words,
And never stops at all,

And sweetest in the gale is heard;
And sore must be the storm
That could abash the little bird
That kept so many warm.

I've heard it in the chillest land,
And on the strangest sea;
Yet, never, in extremity,
It asked a crumb of me.

163

Kitty: What She Thinks of Herself

WILLIAM BRIGHTLY RANDS

I am the Cat of Cats. I am
    The everlasting cat!
Cunning, and old, and sleek as jam,
    The everlasting cat!
I hunt the vermin in the night—
    The everlasting cat!
For I see best without the light—
    The everlasting cat!

The Germ

OGDEN NASH

A mighty creature is the germ,
Though smaller than the pachyderm.
His customary dwelling place
Is deep within the human race.
His childish pride he often pleases
By giving people strange diseases.
Do you, my poppet, feel infirm?
You probably contain a germ.

The Dancing Cabman

J. B. MORTON

Alone on the lawn
    The cabman dances;
In the dew of dawn
    He kicks and prances.
His bowler is set
    On his bullet head.

For his boots are wet,
    And his aunt is dead.
There on the lawn,
    As the light advances,
On the tide of the dawn,
    The cabman dances.

Swift and strong
    As a garden roller,
He dances along
    In his little bowler,
Skimming the lawn
    With royal grace,
The dew of the dawn
    On his great red face.
To fairy flutes,
    As the light advances,
In square black boots
    The cabman dances.

The Sluggard

ISAAC WATTS

'Tis the voice of the Sluggard: I heard him complain,
"You have waked me too soon! I must slumber again!"
As the door on its hinges, so he on his bed
Turns his sides, and his shoulders and his heavy head.

"A little more sleep, and a little more slumber!"
Thus he wastes half his days, and his hours without number;
And when he gets up he sits folding his hands,
Or walks about sauntering, or trifling he stands.

I passed by his garden, and saw the wild brier,
The thorn, and the thistle grow broader and higher;

The clothes that hang on him are turning to rags;
And his money still wastes, till he starves or he begs.

I made him a visit, still hoping to find
He had took better care for improving his mind:
He told me his dreams, talked of eating and drinking;
But he scarce reads his Bible, and never loves thinking.

Said I then to my heart, "Here's a lesson for me!
That man's but a picture of what I might be;
But thanks to my friends for their care in my breeding,
Who have taught me by times to love working and reading!"

Sir Christopher Wren

E. C. BENTLEY

Sir Christopher Wren
Said, "I am going to dine with some men.
If anybody calls,
Say I am designing St. Paul's."

Little Willie

AUTHOR UNKNOWN

Little Willie from his mirror
        Licked the mercury right off,
Thinking, in his childish error,
        It would cure the whooping cough.
At the funeral his mother
        Sadly said to Mrs. Brown:
" 'Twas a chilly day for Willie
When the mercury went down."

Lord Clive

E. C. BENTLEY

What I like about Clive
Is that he is no longer alive.
There is a great deal to be said
For being dead.

Lightly Stepped a Yellow Star

EMILY DICKINSON

Lightly stepped a yellow star
To its lofty place,
Loosed the Moon her silver hat
From her lustral face.

All of evening softly lit
As an astral hall—
"Father," I observed to Heaven,
"You are punctual!"

INDEX OF AUTHORS

169

INDEX OF TITLES

171

172

INDEX OF FIRST LINES